the essential

ibs

COOKBOOK

200 delicious ibs meals to manage symptoms of ibs

LASSELLE PRESS

CONTENTS

SEAFOOD | 57

POULTRY | 91

VEGETARIAN | 128

STOCKS, SOUPS, STEWS AND SAUCES | 160

SIDES, SALADS, SNACKS & SAUCES | 184

DRINKS AND DESSERTS | 204

CONVERSION TABLES | 231
BIBLIOGRAPHY | 233

INTRODUCTION

Welcome to The Essential IBS Cookbook!

Here at Lasselle Press, we understand that experiencing the symptoms of Irritable Bowel Syndrome (IBS) can be uncomfortable at best and excruciating at worst. Furthermore, being diagnosed with IBS and receiving help from your doctor is just the first step in your healing plan; your diet and lifestyle must also change in order to reduce your symptoms and help you live the healthy and happy life you want to.

It's possible you're reading this book because one of your family members suffers from IBS and you want to help them out, or you might suspect that you are experiencing the symptoms of IBS and want to know more about it. It is extremely important to consult your doctor if you notice any of the symptoms outlined later in this book, and we hope that reading this will give you the confidence to go and discuss your symptoms and concerns with a professional.

The first part of this book is aimed at providing you with an understanding of Irritable Bowel Syndrome as well as the possible symptoms, causes and treatments available. From there, we offer advice to go alongside your doctor's or dietician's dietary and medication prescriptions. We provide a comprehensive list of foods to avoid and foods you can continue to enjoy when choosing low FODMAP foods (more on this later in the book). Cooking and lifestyle guidance is also given in order to make the transition to the Low FODMAP diet the easiest and smoothest possible for you during this challenging time.

The rest of this book is dedicated to providing you with healthy and delicious recipes for breakfast, lunch, dinner and dessert that won't leave you feeling uninspired, worn out in the kitchen, or out of budget! In other words, they contain easy-to-find ingredients, simple instructions and delicious outcomes. Each meal is given with its nutritional values broken down in order to help you plan your meals and keep track of what you're eating. Hopefully this will take the strain out of meal planning and preparation, and allow you and the family to enjoy dinner time again!

We wish you all the best in the kitchen and in health!

The Lasselle Press Team

C1: IBS OVERVIEW

IBS affects the large intestine and can cause changes and discomfort during bowel movements. These range in severity from person to person and can be inconvenient, uncomfortable and sometimes even debilitating. Unfortunately the syndrome is incurable but, it can be managed with long term treatment, diet and lifestyle choices.

The exact cause of IBS is unknown, however it may be caused by a problem in the interaction between the gut, the brain and the nervous system. Some factors, such as stress, can worsen symptoms of IBS whilst they do not cause it. Surprisingly very few people seek medical help despite suffering from the symptoms of IBS; in the US, most patients finally seek help around six years after the symptoms of IBS start. It is essential that you do seek a professional diagnosis of IBS if you are concerned that you may be experiencing the symptoms of the syndrome, or if you have a family history of IBS.

According to www.aboutibs.org, 'IBS affects between 25 and 45 million people in the United States.' Of these, two thirds are female. IBS can affect people of all age ranges but is most prevalent in those under 50 years old and can also affect children. Unfortunately it is a syndrome that many are embarrassed to get help for or talk about with their peers due to the nature of the syndrome's symptoms, and thus many end up worsening their symptoms through not getting suitable help and guidance. Treatments are available to help manage IBS and as previously mentioned, changes in your diet and lifestyle can help lessen symptoms which vary from person to person.

So don't lose hope if you've recently been diagnosed, or think you might be suffering from IBS. Seek medical opinion, talk to a trusted family member or friend, and know that there are things that can be changed in order to relieve the pain and discomfort you may be currently feeling.

Symptoms of IBS

There are a variety of symptoms associated with IBS and these can often coincide. These include:

- Diarrhoea

- Constipation

- Abdominal pain and cramping

- Gas

- Feeling bloated

- Mucus in the stool

You should seek out medical help if you develop symptoms of rectal bleeding, abdominal pain that becomes severely worse at night, or unexplained weight loss. These are symptoms that could worsen the overall effects of IBS, or could point to more serious underlying issues with your health.

There are two categories of IBS:

IBS-D - resulting in diarrhoea symptoms.

IBS-C - resulting in constipation symptoms.

Although there are two categories, it is important to remember that your symptoms can alternate and shift between the two.

IBS Triggers

Although as previously mentioned, the exact cause of IBS is unknown, we know how it occurs in comparison to a healthy intestinal tract system in a person without IBS: layers of muscle line the walls of our intestines that either contract or relax in order to move the food we consume from our stomach all the way down to our rectum, through the intestinal tract. With IBS, these contractions may either be stronger, lasting longer than usual, thus causing gas, bloating, and diarrhoea, or they may be weaker and slower than usual, thus causing constipation.

There are many different triggers for the symptoms of IBS to occur and these range from person to person, and can also change over time for a particular indi-vidual. It is important to keep all possible triggers in mind because of IBS being a terribly unpredictable syndrome. Some of the most common triggers are:

•   Specific foods - this can vary between individuals.

•   Food allergies or intolerances e.g. chocolate, spices, fat, beans, fruits, cauliflower, cabbage, broccoli, milk, soda, carbonated drinks, alcohol etc.

- Stress - triggers an over-active nervous system which can intensify the signals sent to the gastrointestinal area of the body and cause stronger contractions.

- Hormones - particularly worsening during a woman's menstrual cycle.

- Other illnesses e.g. anxiety or depression.

- Excess intestinal bacteria - can interfere with the digestion process and contribute to IBS symptoms.

Other Conditions Linked To IBS

What makes diagnosing and treating IBS a little complicated is that there are other conditions and diseases that are linked to IBS. These can produce similar symptoms and in some cases worsen IBS symptoms. Please discuss these conditions and symptoms with your doctor in order to get specific treatment.

SIBO - a condition linked to and associated with IBS. SIBO stands for Small Intestine Bacteria Overgrowth. This overgrowth can interfere with the digestion process and absorption of food as well as damage the membrane lining. It is healthy to have a certain amount of bacteria in our gut. In this case, however there is an excessive amount of bacteria; this can cause chronic fatigue, body pains, and stress on the liver. Through the damage caused to the membrane lining, larger food particles are able to pass through without being properly digested; this can cause food allergies and sensitivities. If you are diagnosed and treated for SIBO, your IBS symptoms may also be alleviated.

Celiac Disease - another condition linked to IBS. Celiac Disease causes a sensitivity to gluten. Gluten is a protein that is contained in barley, rye, and wheat products. Celiac disease can cause symptoms such as anemia, fatigue, diarrhoea, bloating and weight loss, which can sometimes lead to serious complications. Celiac disease can worsen IBS symptoms.

In the next chapter we will discuss dietary and lifestyle changes you can make in order to help relieve the symptoms of IBS.

C2 -DIET AND LIFESTYLE GUIDANCE

Along with the treatment prescribed by your doctor and their guidance, making changes to your diet and lifestyle can have an extremely positive effect on your symptoms and thus your lifestyle. There are a number of different diets that have been recommended for IBS sufferers and each person will react differently to certain foods, so it is important to bear this in mind. Be mindful of which foods trigger your symptoms as well as those that do not; you can do this by keeping a journal of the foods and drinks you eat as well as your symptoms experienced daily. This method will allow you to notice if there are any patterns with certain foods or ingredients that may be triggering symptoms.

This cookbook uses low FODMAP foods as the diet that is most commonly now recommended for those with IBS. Again, this may vary from patient to patient and it is imperative to seek dietary guidance from a professional before changing your diet. Information about the low FODMAP diet will be given in the next section so that you can find out more about it.

The Low FODMAP Diet

FODMAPs stand for Fermentable, Oligio-, Di-, Mono-saccharides And Polyols. FODMAPs are carbohydrates with short chains that naturally occur in food and are not properly absorbed through the small intestine. Choosing foods and portion sizes that are low in FODMAPs can greatly reduce the triggering of symptoms.

Use the following lists of foods to select foods and portion sizes that are classed as Low FODMAP.
Avoid those that are classed as high FODMAP.
Please note, whilst some foods may be classed as low FODMAP, this can depend on the portion size. Take note of the portion sizes for each type of food and ingredient so that you don't go over the recommended serving sizes.

Fruits:

LOW FODMAP – Enjoy (stick to 1 fruit/1 cup per serving whichever is the smaller quantity):
Banana (1/2 large banana serving/approx. 30g),
Blueberries – buy organic,
Boysenberry – buy organic,
Cantaloupe,
Star fruit,
Cranberry – buy organic,
Durian, Grapes – buy organic,
Grapefruit,
Honeydew melon,
Kiwi, Lemon,
Lime,
Mandarin,
Orange,
Passion fruit,
Paw paw,
Pineapple,
Raspberry – buy organic,
Rhubarb,
Strawberry – buy organic,
Tangelo

HIGH FODMAP – Avoid – (any fruits of more than 1 cup per serving) plus:
Apple,
Mango,
Nashi fruit,
Pear,
Persimmon,
Rambutan,
Watermelon,
Persimmon,
Rambutan,
Apricot,

Avocado,
Blackberries,
Cherries,
Longon,
Lychee,
Nashi Fruit,
Nectarine,
Peach,
Pear,
Plum,
Prune,
Watermelon

VEGETABLES: Enjoy (stick to 1 vegetable/1 cup per serving whichever is the smaller quantity):
Alfalfa,
Bamboo shoots,
Bean shoots,
Beans (green),
Bok Choy,
Capsicum,
Carrot (1 medium carrot),
Celery, Chives,
Choy Sum,
Cucumber,
Endive,
Fennel heart (1 small heart or smaller 49g),
Ginger,
Lettuce (may be ok for some),
Marrow,
Olives,
Parsnip,
Parsley,
Potato (2 small potatoes),
Pumpkin (1/2 cup),
Silverbeet,
Spring onion (green section only),

Spinach (1 cup),
Swede,
Sweet potato (3 tbsp.),
Taro,
Beef tomatoes,
Turnip,
Yam,
Zucchini (this may be okay for some; check individual tolerance),
Chives, spring onion and scallions (green tips only)

Avoid (any vegetables of more than 1 cup per serving) plus:
Artichokes (Globe & Jerusalem),
Asparagus,
Beet,
Broccoli,
Brussel Sprouts, Cabbage, Chicory, Dandelion leaves, Fennel, Garlic, Leek, Legumes, Okra, Onion (brown, white, & Spanish), Peas, Radicchio Lettuce, Shallots, Spring onion (white section), Squash , Avocado, Cauliflower, Mushrooms, Snow peas, Sugar Snap Peas, Corn, Eggplant, Cherry Tomatoes (due to mould), Onion (brown, white & Spanish), Onion powder, White section of spring onion, Leeks, Shallots, Garlic.

Please note: there is undeclared onion hidden in many processed foods including, chicken salt, vegetable salt, vegetable powder, dehydrated vegetables, stocks, gravies, soups, marinades, & sauces. Make sure you check ingredients labels for packaged items and avoid onion.

Flavorings & Herbs & Spices
Enjoy:
Golden Syrup, Treacle, Molasses, Maple Syrup, White, Brown, Raw & Castor Sugar, (sucrose) eaten in moderation, Tea, & Herbal Teas, Seeds (in moderation), Oat bran (max 1/4 cup serving), Rolled Oats (max 1/4 cup serving), Gluten Free Oats, Barley Bran, Psyllium, Rice Bran, Suitable Sweeteners (nutrasweet, sucralose, aspartame, stevia, saccharine, tic tacs, minties, regular gum), Baking Cocoa Powder, Carob Powder, Olive Oil, Canola Oil, Garlic-infused Oil, Coconut Oil, Unsweetened Desiccated Coconut (max 1/4 cup serving), Fresh & dried Ginger, Cilantro, Basil, Lemongrass, Mint, Parsley, Marjoram, Thyme, Rosemary & other herbs.

Avoid:

Honey, Corn syrups, Corn Syrup Solids, Fruisana, Chickory, Dandelion Tea, Artificial Sweeteners, Sugar free or Low Carb Sweets, Mints or Gums, Dairy Desserts, Baked Beans, Lentils, Chickpeas, processed foods, Coconut, Solid Chocolate, Solid Carob, Olives, Nuts and Nut Butters, Caffeine, Decaf Coffee.

Dairy & Other
Enjoy:

Egg whites, Rice milk, Almond Milk, Raw Goats milk, Hemp milk, Goats cheese, Cottage cheese

Avoid:

Other cheeses, Egg yolks, Dairy – milk, Cream, Yogurt, Butter, Other Oils, Sour cream, Soy milk, Coconut milk.

Wheat Products & Alternatives:
Enjoy:

Rice, , Potato, Amaranth, Tapioca, Quinoa, Millet, Sorghum, Buckwheat, Arrowroot, Sago, Gluten Free (GF) Bread, Gluten Free Pasta, Rice Noodles, Wheat Free Buckwheat Noodles, Porridge, Wheat Free Muesli, Rice Bubbles, Gluten Free Cereals, Rice Cakes & Crackers, GF crackers, Ryvitas, & Rye Cruskits, GF cakes, Flourless Cakes, GF biscuits, GF Pastry Mixes, & Bread Crumbs, Polenta, Buckwheat, Millet, Rice Flours, Oats & Barley.

Avoid:

Bread (white, wholemeal, multigrain, sourdough, pita, & many rye), Pasta & n=Noodles (regular, two minute, spelt, egg noodles, hokkien & udon), Breakfast Cereals (containing wheat, excess dried fruit &/or fruit juice), Savoury Biscuits (wheat based), Cakes & Baked Goods (wheat based), Biscuits (wheat based), Pastry & Breadcrumbs (wheat flour made), Others (semolina, couscous, bulgur).

Protein Sources:
Enjoy:

Oily Fish, Lean Meats e.g. Skinless Chicken or Turkey Breasts

Avoid:

Red meat, Dark Meat from Poultry e.g. turkey/chicken thighs, Soy Products e.g. tofu/tempeh

Lifestyle Guidance:

Along with a diet that prevents or lessens the trigger of your IBS symptoms, other lifestyle changes can help you to feel healthier and less stressed, thus alleviating symptoms further.

1.   Ensure you exercise regularly - 20-30 minutes oer day or 2-3 times per week will boost serotonin levels, helping you to feel happier and less stressed. Additionally you will feel great physically and prevent other serious illnesses such as obesity and heart disease.

2.   Eat your meals slowly and mindfully. In other words, not at your computer on a 'working lunch', rushing to pick up the kids, or on the way to work. This will help your digestive system and help to prevent the symptoms such as cramps and bloating.

3.   Avoid chewing gum, especially when you're not eating soon after. The saliva that builds in your mouth sends a signal to your stomach that you are about to eat, if this is not the case it confuses the digestive system and can trigger symptoms.

4.   Drink plenty of water! This greatly improves general health as well as assisting the digestive system in flushing out slow to move particles and preventing constipation.

5.   Evaluate your work/life balance. Is the commute causing you unnecessary stress and is there someone who can possibly help with the childcare or chores in any way? Can you cut down on unnecessary expenses so that you have more money to pay for these things. Whatever helps prevent or cut down stress can have a dramatic effect on your symptoms.

6.   Try to get plenty of sleep by winding down at least one hour before you would like to be asleep and turning off all computers and electronic devices. Use an alarm clock rather than your phone and turn off anything electric at the wall; the blue lighting and signals can interfere with your brain waves and keep you alert when you want to be fast asleep!

7.   IBS can be a source of embarrassment to many sufferers and many end up concealing their symptoms or avoiding situations because of them. IBS can really affect the way you get along with everyday life. Reach out to a local support

group or to online forums if you don't want to discuss it with family and friends. Talk to your doctors for advice. If you can, tell someone at work who you feel you can trust so that you don't find yourself having to make up excuses for sick days or whilst there. You will be surprised at how understanding your colleagues and employers can be!

8.   Consider therapies - counselling can be extremely helpful; as with any other physical or mental illness, IBS can cause mental and physical symptoms. Consider cognitive behavioural therapy, hypnotherapy, biofeedback and others. Your local support group, doctors or the internet may be able to help you work out what type of therapy would benefit you the most.

9.   Take a look at your medications - some medications prescribed to you may actually be worsening the symptoms of IBS including: antibiotics, some antidepressants, medicine containing sorbitol such as cough syrups, prozac, sarafem and zoloft can cause diarrhoea. Speak to your doctors about any current medication you're on and whether they these can be adjusted to your needs. Always consult your doctor before discontinuing any medications.

C3: EATING OUT AND SHOPPING GUIDE

Advice for Dining Out

It can be very hard for you to dine out with friends and family if you suffer from IBS; you never know when your symptoms might be triggered and what foods may or may not be available. Not only that but how your dishes are cooked might even trigger your symptoms. These are probably just a few of the worries that go through your mind before going out and many people will avoid going out altogether due to their embarrassment or painful symptoms.

But you don't have to miss out on your favorite restaurant or cuisines! Here are a few tips that may make dining out easier for you:

- Research the restaurant's menu beforehand and decide what you will choose to avoid anxiety and spontaneous decisions that you will regret later.
- Use the food lists in the previous chapter to help you choose and don't feel bad about asking the restaurant to cater to your needs.
- Take the Low FODMAP lists along and share this with the restaurant so they

are well-informed of your needs.
- Ask your server for your foods to be cooked without extra salts, butters or sauces.
- Avoid fried foods and opt for grilled or poached instead.
- Avoid drinking alcohol and opt for water or lemonade instead.
- Eat slowly and pace yourself between courses.
- Take any medication you have been prescribed at the usual time.

Advice for traveling

1. Whatever your travel plans, you will have to eat. If you plan ahead, you should be able to make a meal plan that suits your need.
2. If you have a dietitian, tell them where you are going and what you expect to eat at your destination.
3. Remember to pack enough of any prescription medicines you must take.
4. If going on a road trip or camping, avoid processed meats and foods. rom the Low FODMAP lists.
5. Take snacks suitable for the low FODMAP diet to avoid picking up treats from the service stations!
6. Do not consume dairy products.
7. If you are going on a cruise, all those buffet foods are tempting to eat 24 hours a day. To help with this predicament try to select fruits, salads, and vegetables from the lists.
8. Let the cruise line or hotel know of your dietary needs, most are willing to prepare special foods for you.
9. If you are going to be traveling abroad and don't speak the language, bring a phrasebook that has a section for ordering food.
10. Check if you can check in early and check out late to avoid waiting around for flight times.

Cooking Tips

1. *Grill, poach, roast or sauté meats instead of frying.*
2. *Steam or boil vegetables instead of frying.*
3. *Use healthy oils such as extra virgin olive oil or coconut oil to shallow fry.*
4. *Avoid added sugars and opt for Stevia instead of sugar.*

Useful Kitchen Equipment

The following items will be useful in cooking the recipes in this cookbook :

- A selection of non-stick skillets,
- A large pot for soups and stews,
- A Slow Cooker,
- A set of Tupperware for storage and bulk cooking,
- Food Processor/blender/pestle and mortar,
- Large Bowls for salads or mixing.

One Last Thing

Always remember to use new recipes and ingredients after speaking to your doctor or dietitian; your needs will be unique to you depending on your symptoms and the certain foods that trigger them.
We hope that with your doctor's advice, along with our guidance and recipes, that you can continue to enjoy cooking, eating and sharing meal times with your love ones.

Thank you for purchasing this book and we wish you all the best on your path to health and contentment.

Happy cooking!

BREAKFAST

Strawberry Oats

SERVES 1 / PREP TIME: 5 MINUTES / COOK TIME: 15 MINUTES

Delicious pops of sweetness combine with the crunch of the muesli in this simple breakfast recipe.

2 tbsp wheat-free muesli for topping (optional)
1 tsp maple syrup
1/4 cup organic strawberries, sliced
¼ cup rolled oats (or gluten-free if celiac)

½ cup almond milk

1. Preheat the oven to its highest setting.
2. Combine the maple syrup with the muesli and layer across a lined baking tray.
3. Place in the oven for 10 minutes or until crunchy.
4. Combine the oats and rice milk and cook in a pan over a low heat for 3-4 minutes or according to package directions (alternatively pop this in the microwave for 1 minute).
5. Serve and scatter with strawberries and the crunchy muesli topping.

Hint: Make extra crunchy muesli and store in an airtight container for up to 2 weeks. It makes a great addition to any breakfast.

Per serving: Calories: 417 Protein: 11g Carbs: 79g Fiber: 9g Sugar: 24g Fat: 7g

Banana & Cocoa Oatmeal Pancakes

SERVES 2 / PREP TIME: 10 MINUTES / COOK TIME: 15 MINUTES

Filling and sweet – great for breakfast and dessert!

2 large egg whites
1 ½ cup of rolled oats (gluten-free if celiac)
½ cup almond milk
1 medium banana
1 tsp vanilla extract
2 tbsp baking cocoa powder

2 tsp coconut oil

1. First, blend together the egg whites, oats, almond milk, banana and vanilla extract in a food processor until you get a smooth mixture.
2. Pour your mixture into a medium sized bowl and then add the cocoa powder.
3. Heat 1 tsp. of the oil in a large skillet on a medium heat.
4. Once the oil is hot, pour half of your pancake batter into the skillet and leave for 4-5 minutes.
5. Use a spatula to gently place under the edges of the pancake – if it comes away from the skillet easily then flip the pancake over and continue to cook for 2-3 minutes.
6. Lower the heat if needed to prevent burning.
7. Repeat for the second pancake.
8. Top with a little maple syrup if desired.

Hint: You could try swapping the oats for the same amount of rice milk and make banana crepes instead.

Per serving: Calories: 360 Protein: 14g Carbs: 62g Fiber: 10g Sugar: 12g Fat: 8g

Homemade Granola

SERVES 2 / PREP TIME: 5 MINUTES / COOK TIME: 40 MINUTES

It can be extremely difficult to find cereals when you're suffering with IBS; the good news is that it is so simple to make!

---

1 cup rolled oats (gluten-free if need-ed)
1 tbsp uncooked quinoa
1 tbsp. flax seeds
1 cup organic raspberries
zest of 1 orange
1 tbsp maple syrup
1 tsp stevia powder

1 tbsp. coconut oil (melted)

---

1. Preheat the oven to 300ºF/ 150ºC/Gas Mark 2.
2. Mix the oats, quinoa, flax seeds, raspberries and orange zest in a large bowl.
3. Add the maple syrup, sugar and oil and stir until combined.
4. Layer the mix across a lined baking tray.
5. Bake in the oven for 35-40 minutes, mixing occasionally with a wooden spoon.
6. The granola should be golden brown and smelling delicious by now!
7. Remove from the oven and allow to cool before serving.
8. Enjoy on its own or with your choice of dairy-free milk.

Hint: This can be stored in an airtight container for up to two weeks, so go ahead and make in bulk to save time! You can also substitute raspberries for any LOW FODMAP fruit of your choice.

Per serving: Calories: 333 Protein: 8g Carbs: 51g Fiber: 10g Sugar: 10g Fat: 12g

Spinach and Goats Cheese Frittata

SERVES 5 / PREP TIME: 10 MINUTES / COOK TIME: 25 MINUTES

A tasty start to the day!

---

2 small white potatoes, peeled and
sliced
1 tsp olive oil
4 cups baby spinach
1 tsp canola oil
5 egg whites
½ cup goats cheese
1 tbsp parsley (dried or fresh)
A pinch of salt and pepper to taste

---

1. Add the sliced potatoes to a pan of boiling water over a high heat and boil for 7-8 minutes.
2. Meanwhile, heat the olive oil in a non-stick skillet over a medium heat.
3. Next, add the baby spinach to the skillet and cook for 5 minutes or until wilted.
4. Drain any excess water from the skillet and place spinach to one side.
5. Now drain the potatoes and allow to cool slightly.
6. Reheat the skillet and add the canola oil.
7. Sauté the potato slices for 5-6 minutes or until golden.
8. Preheat your broiler/grill on high and whisk together the egg whites, goats cheese, spinach, parsley and salt and pepper.
9. Pour the egg mixture into the skillet with the potatoes.
10. Place under the broiler/grill for 10 minutes until eggs are thoroughly cooked through and the top is golden and bubbling.
11. Slice into five portions and enjoy!

Per serving: Calories: 120 Protein: 9g Carbs: 8g Fiber: 2g Sugar: 1g Fat: 6g

Buckwheat Porridge with Grapefruit

SERVES 2 / PREP TIME: 5 MINUTES / COOK TIME: 25 MINUTES

Buckwheat is a LOW FODMAP alternative for breakfast and tastes amazing.

---

1 cup buckwheat groats
2 cups rice/almond/hemp milk
1 cup fresh grapefruit, sliced
2 tsp. brown sugar

---

1. Over a medium heat, combine the buckwheat and milk in a pot and bring to a simmer.
2. Cook with the lid on for 18-20 minutes.
3. The buckwheat will have soaked up most of the milk once done.
4. Remove and serve with the sliced grapefruit and a sprinkle of stevia powder to counteract the sour taste of the grapefruit.

Per serving: Calories: 361 Protein: 10g Carbs: 76g Fiber: 9g Sugar: 26g Fat: 4g

Low-Carb Chia Pumpkin Flapjacks

SERVES 4 / PREP TIME: 10 MINUTES / COOK TIME: 10 MINUTES

These hearty oat, chia, and pumpkin flapjacks will start your day off right!

1 tbsp chia seeds
1 tbsp golden flax seed meal
2 tbsp maple syrup
1/4 cup unsweetened cashew/almond/
rice milk
1 pinch salt
1/2 tsp pumpkin pie spice
1/2 cup canned pumpkin puree

1/4 cup rice flour
olive oil cooking spray

1. In a medium sized bowl, combine the chia seeds, the golden flax seed meal, the syrup, and the cashew milk.
2. Let this mixture sit for 5 minutes.
3. Next, fold in the salt, the pumpkin pie spice, the pumpkin puree, and the rice flour.
4. Mix everything in the bowl thoroughly.
5. Meanwhile, heat your pan or griddle to medium heat.
6. Spray with olive oil cooking spray.
7. Now pour the flapjack mixture into the pan or griddle in four evenly sized circles.
8. Spread each circle with a spatula until it reaches about 2-3 inches in diameter.
9. Cook over medium heat for 4-5 minutes.
10. Flip the flapjack over and cook the other side for the same amount of time.
11. To serve, drizzle with the maple syrup.

Hint: Use a nonstick surface, like a nonstick frying pan or griddle, to prevent the flapjacks from sticking.

Per serving: Calories: 108   Protein: 2g Carbs: 20g Sugar: 9g Fat: 2g

Sunrise Pancakes

SERVES 4 / PREP TIME: 10 MINUTES / COOK TIME: 10 MINUTES

This delightful combination of sesame seeds and banana is sure to power up your morning!

1 tbsp sesame seeds
1/4 cup steel cut oats (gluten-free)
1 medium ripe banana
1 egg white
1/2 tsp ground ginger
1 tbsp coconut flakes
olive oil cooking spray

1. In a clean spice or coffee grinder, blend the sesame seeds and oats until the combination has a flourlike texture.
2. In a separate small food processor, blend together the banana, the egg white, and the ginger until it the mixture is smooth.
3. Pour the oat and sesame flour into the banana batter and blend in the food processor again until all is thoroughly combined.
4. After blending, take the food processor bowl off and mix in the coconut flakes with a spoon.
5. Set aside the batter so it can thicken.
6. While the batter thickens, preheat your frying pan or griddle and spray with olive oil cooking spray.
7. Divide the batter into four pancakes in the pan.
8. Spread out each pancake with a spatula to about 3 inches in diameter.
9. Cook the pancakes over medium heat for 4-5 minutes on the first side.
10. Flip them with a spatula and cook them about 3-4 minutes on the second side, until they are golden brown.
11. Serve.

Tip: Instead of using a food processor, you can mash the ripe banana with a fork and briskly whisk the egg white and cinnamon through until the mixture is smooth.

Per serving: Calories: 99 Protein: 2g Carbs: 12g Fiber: 2g Sugar: 4g Fat: 2g

Hearty Homemade Energy Bars

SERVES 8 / PREP TIME: 10 MINUTES / COOK TIME: 30 MINUTES

These easy energy bars are sure to make snack time fun and healthy.

3/4 cup oat flour
1/4 cup unsweetened coconut flakes
1/2 tsp baking powder
1 ripe banana, mashed
1/4 cup maple syrup

1/2 tsp vanilla extract
1/4 cup dry roasted pumpkin seeds
1/4 cup dry roasted sunflower seeds, hulled
1/8 cup chia seeds

1. Preheat the oven to 350 degrees.
2. Line an 8x8 oven-safe dish with parchment paper.
3. Combine the oat flour, the coconut flakes, the baking powder, the mashed banana, the maple syrup, and the vanilla extract in a large bowl and mix thoroughly.
4. Stir in the pumpkin seeds, the sunflower seeds, and the chia seeds.
5. Mix everything together until well combined.
6. Scrape the mixture into the lined baking dish and level it out with wet fingers.
7. Bake for 20 minutes at 350 degrees.
8. Turn the oven off.
9. Allow the mixture to sit in the warm oven for 5-10 minutes.
10. Remove the dish and allow it to cool on a wire rack.
11. Once it has cooled, turn the baked mixture onto a cutting board.
12. Slice into 8 bars and serve!

Per serving: Calories: 177 Protein: 5g Carbs: 26g Sugar: 9g Fat: 7g

Kiwi Chia Parfait

SERVES 6 / PREP TIME: 10 MINUTES / COOK TIME: NA / CHILL: OVERNIGHT

This breakfast treat is ready as soon as you wake up!

1/4 cup chia seeds
1/4 cup unsweetened coconut flakes
1 1/4 cup unsweetened light coconut milk
2 tbsp maple syrup
1 medium banana, mashed
3 kiwis, peeled and sliced

1 dash vanilla extract
1 pinch salt

---

1. Combine the chia seeds and the coconut in a large bowl.
2. Pour in the rest of the ingredients.
3. Stir everything in the bowl thoroughly, making sure the banana is smoothly incorporated.
4. Arrange the kiwi slices in alternating layers with the chia mixture in 6 sundae glasses or parfait bowls.
5. Cover with plastic wrap or aluminum foil.
6. Place in the refrigerator overnight.
7. Take out a spoon and enjoy first thing!

Hint: If you don't have sundae glasses or parfait bowls, you can substitute them with pint-sized mason jars.

Per serving: Calories: 149 Protein: 3g Carbs: 11g Sugar: 10g Fat: 8g

Tomato and Chive Frittata

SERVES 2 / PREP TIME: 10 MINUTES / COOK TIME: 20 MINUTES

This Mediterranean-style breakfast will start your day right!

4 egg whites
6 tbsp unsweetened rice milk or water
1 pinch salt
1/2 cup fresh spinach, loosely chopped

1/2 fresh red bell pepper, diced
1/2 cup fresh roma tomatoes, diced
1/4 cup crumbled goat cheese
2 tbsp chives (green tips only), sliced

1. Whisk the egg whites in a large bowl until frothy.
2. Add in the milk and the salt.
3. Whisk these together until thoroughly combined.
4. Mix in the rest of the ingredients and stir well.
5. Meanwhile, preheat the oven to 350 degrees.
6. Place an oven-safe frying pan with a matching lid on the stovetop over medium heat.
7. Once the pan is warm, pour in the egg mixture.
8. Cover with the lid.
9. Let this pan sit over medium heat without stirring for about 5 minutes.
10. Next, place the pan in the oven.
11. Let it bake for 10-15 minutes.
12. Keep checking to see if the frittata is done. It is cooked when the top is no longer runny.
13. Remove from the oven.
14. Take off the lid and allow it to cool for a couple of minutes before serving.

Per serving: Calories: 236 Protein: 18g Carbs: 16g Sugar: 12g Fat: 12g

Vegetarian Miso Pasta To Go

SERVES 2 / PREP TIME: 10 MINUTES / COOK TIME: 2 MINUTES

This jarred dinner can be made ahead of time and grabbed for an on-the-go meal.

1/2 tsp miso paste	1 (8 oz) bags rice vermicelli noodles (or
1/4 tsp onion infused olive oil	equivalent gluten free noodle)
1/4 tsp garlic infused olive oil	1 tbsp fresh chopped cilantro leaves
1/2 cup chopped Swiss chard	1 tbsp fresh minced scallions, green tips
1/4 cup finely grated carrot	2 wedges lemon
4 tbsp rinsed canned sweet corn	3-4 cups boiling water

---

1. Gather two 2 ¼ cup-capacity glass jars that are heatproof and can be sealed.
2. In a small bowl, mix together the miso paste and infused oils, then spread this mixture over the bottom of each jar.
3. Layer the rest of the ingredients equally in each jar as follows: the Swiss chard, the grated carrot, the sweet corn, the vermicelli noodles, the cilantro leaves, the scallions, and a wedge of lemon.
4. Pour 1 ½ - 2 cups of boiling water over the contents of each jar.
5. Let the noodles cook in the water for 2 minutes before enjoying.

Hint: You can infuse your own olive oil by adding dried herbs to a jar of olive oil, sealing, storing it for a week, then straining.

Per serving: Calories: 138 Protein: 3 Carbs: 27 Sugar: 2 Fat: 2

Strawberry Chocolate Chia Pudding

SERVES 2 / PREP TIME: 5 MINUTES / COOK TIME: NA CHILL TIME: OVERNIGHT

A winning combination gives you something to look forward to when you wake up!

---

1 cup unsweetened cashew milk
1 ½ tsp maple syrup
1 tsp vanilla extract
1 tbsp unsweetened cocoa powder
2 tbsp chia seeds
1 cup fresh strawberries, sliced
2 tbsp unsweetened coconut flakes

---

1. Whisk the cashew milk, maple syrup, vanilla extract, and cocoa powder together in a bowl.
2. Keep whisking until the cocoa powder is well integrated.
3. Stir in the chia seeds.
4. Pour into a glass jar.
5. Tightly cover with a lid.
6. Refrigerate overnight.
7. Just before serving, stir the pudding well to break up any lumps.
8. Pour the pudding into 2 serving bowls.
9. Scatter the sliced strawberries and the coconut flakes on top.
10. Store this pudding up to 5 days in the fridge.

Hint: Add other low FODMAP toppings of your choice to mix this breakfast up.

Per serving: Calories: 149 Protein: 5g Carbs: 19g Sugar: 8g Fat: 7g

Homemade Millet Hot Cereal

SERVES 4 / PREP TIME: 5 MINUTES / COOK TIME: 25 MINUTES

This warming porridge fits perfectly in any balanced breakfast.

---

1 cup hulled millet seeds
1 cup unsweetened light coconut milk
1 ½ cups boiling water
Pinch of salt

Topping Choices:
1 cup unsweetened light coconut milk
1 ripe banana
2 cups raspberries
1/2 cup pineapple chunks
1 tbsp maple syrup

---

1. Toast the millet seeds in a medium saucepan over medium high heat for about 2-3 minutes, or until they start to turn a golden color.
2. Add the milk, boiling water, and salt.
3. Cover and bring to a simmer.
4. Once the saucepan is boiling, turn down the heat to the lowest setting.
5. Allow the pan to simmer for 15 to 20 minutes, or until most of the liquid absorbs and the millet is soft.
6. Turn off the burner.
7. After it's done cooking, stir more milk into the millet until the porridge is creamy.
8. Meanwhile, peel and slice the banana.
9. Gather the raspberries and pineapple chunks.
10. Divide the porridge among 4 bowls.
11. Top each bowl with the banana, raspberries, and pineapple slices.
12. Drizzle maple syrup over the fruit and serve.

Tip: You can include any other low FODMAP topping you like on top of this hot cereal, such as blueberries, strawberries, and so on.

Per serving: Calories: 375   Protein: 8 Carbs: 67 Sugar: 15 Fat: 11

Fresh Zucchini-Carrot Mini Frittatas

SERVES 5 / PREP TIME: 15 MINUTES / COOK TIME: 30 MINUTES

These muffin-sized frittatas are great to make ahead of time and eat for breakfast all week

---

2 large carrots, peeled and diced
1/4 cup olive oil
4 large egg whites
1 1/4 cups almond/rice milk
2 tsp garlic infused olive oil
1/2 tsp ground turmeric

3/4 cup gluten-free all purpose baking flour
1 cup diced scallions (green tips)
1/3 cup fresh cilantro leaves, chopped
1 cup zucchini, grated
1 cup canned chickpeas, drained & rinsed
salt and pepper to taste

---

1. Preheat the oven to 350 degrees.
2. Place a large frying pan over medium heat.
3. Meanwhile, peel and dice the carrots.
4. Add the carrots to the frypan with a drizzle of the olive oil.
5. Allow the carrots to gently sauté for 10 to 15 minutes, or until soft and slightly golden brown, stirring occasionally.
6. Whisk together in a large bowl the egg whites, milk, and garlic infused oil.
7. Next, sprinkle in the the turmeric and the flour, whisking until it is all combined.
8. Mix the grated zucchini, scallions, chickpeas, cilantro, and cooked carrot into the bowl with the egg white mixture.
9. Season this mixture with salt and pepper to taste, then mix it again.
10. Meanwhile, line one 12-muffin tin with muffin papers.
11. Spoon the frittata batter into each muffin cup, filling each cup almost to the top.
12. Place the muffin tin in the oven and cook for 25 to 30 minutes.
13. They are done when each mini frittata is springy and golden, or a skewer comes out clean.

Hint: It's normal for the frittatas to sink after coming out of the oven.

Tip: These will keep in the fridge for two days or longer in the freezer.

Per serving: Calories: 286 Protein: 9g Carbs: 33g Sugar: 8g Fat: 14g

Blueberries and Cream Rice Pudding

SERVES 4 / PREP TIME: 5 MINUTES / COOK TIME: 1 1/2 HOURS

If you like rice pudding, this blueberry variation will really satisfy your taste buds.

1/2 cup short grain white rice
1 1/2 tbsp chia seeds
2 cups canned light coconut milk
3 cups hemp milk
1/4 cup water

1/2 tsp ground ginger
maple syrup to taste
2 cups organic blueberries
1/3 cup water

---

1. Preheat the oven to 320 degrees.
2. Place the rice, chia seeds, coconut milk, hemp milk, water, and ginger in a 9x13 baking dish.
3. Combine these ingredients together in the dish.
4. Place the dish in the oven, uncovered.
5. Cook for 1 ½ hours, stirring every 20 to 30 minutes to break up the skin that forms on top.
6. Remove the dish once the rice feels thick and creamy like rice pudding.
7. Place the rice pudding to one side and it allow to cool for a few minutes.
8. Meanwhile, while the rice is in the oven, place the blueberries into a small saucepan.
9. Add the 1/3 cup water to the blueberries and cover the pan with a lid.
10. Place it over medium heat for 5-6 minutes, or until the fruit is soft.
11. Check the pudding to see if it has cooled down.
12. Stir the maple syrup into the pudding, if desired.
13. Serve the creamed rice and stewed blueberries in the same bowl.

Per serving: Calories: 291   Protein: 5g Carbs: 39g Sugar: 11g Fat: 14g

Feta Omelet With Roasted Tomato Sauce

SERVES 2 / PREP TIME: 5 MINUTES / COOK TIME: 1 HOUR INCLUDING SAUCE

This saucy take on the traditional omelet is sure to surprise your taste buds.

---

2 tbsp olive oil
3 beef tomatoes, sliced
1 sprig fresh thyme
1 sprig fresh rosemary
salt and pepper to taste
1/2 tsp stevia powder

1 tbsp garlic infused olive oil
10 egg whites
salt to taste
1 tbsp chopped fresh parsley
1 tbsp garlic infused oil
2 oz crumbled feta cheese

---

1. Preheat the oven to 400 degrees.
2. Oil the bottom of a 9x13 baking dish with some of the olive oil.
3. Arrange the sliced tomatoes in this dish in a single layer.
4. Tuck the thyme and rosemary sprigs in among the tomato slices.
5. Sprinkle the tomatoes with the salt, the pepper, and the stevia.
6. Drizzle the rest of the olive oil and the garlic infused oil over the tomatoes.
7. Roast the tomatoes in the hot oven, uncovered, for 40-50 minutes.
8. When the tomatoes are done roasting, remove the thyme and rosemary sprigs.
9. Tip the entire contents of the dish into a food processor.
10. Blend until the tomatoes are smooth, then pour the sauce through a strainer into a clean frying pan.
11. Start the omelet by cracking the egg whites into a clean bowl.
12. Beat them with a whisk or fork before adding the salt, pepper, and parsley.
13. Heat the garlic oil in a wide non-stick frying pan over medium heat.
14. Add the eggs to the pan and turn the heat to low for 10 minutes.
15. Next, lift the edges of the omelet slightly to make sure it easily lifts away from the pan.
16. Sprinkle the crumbled feta over the face of the omelet.
17. Take a spatula and lift one side of the omelet so that you can fold it over.
18. To serve, cut the omelet in half and place each side on a plate with a spoonful of the roasted tomato sauce.

Hint: If the omelet has started to stick, this means your heat is too high. To prevent this, make sure you use enough ghee and only a low heat.

Per serving: Calories: 453 Protein: 25g Carbs: 15g Fiber: 4g Sugar: 11g Fat: 34g

Herbed Green Onion Scrambled Eggs

SERVES 4 / PREP TIME: 5 MINUTES / COOK TIME: 10 MINUTES

This herbed variation on the breakfast classic makes the perfect brunch dish!

---

1 tsp coconut oil
4 egg whites
salt to taste
1 tbsp fresh basil
1 tbsp sliced green onion
To Serve:
2 gluten free English muffins
2 large tomatoes, halved

---

1. Heat the oil in a skillet over medium-low heat.
2. Crack the eggs and separate the whites from the yolks.
3. Sprinkle in the salt, pepper, basil, and green onion.
4. Whisk this egg white mixture with a fork or whisk.
5. Once the oil is melted, pour the egg white mixture into the pan.
6. Cook for about 10 minutes on low heat.
7. Stir continuously with a non-stick spatula for scrambled eggs.
8. Meanwhile, roast the tomato halves under a broiler set on low for about 5 minutes.
9. Cut the muffins in half and toast them in the toaster or in the broiler alongside the tomatoes.
10. Layer each plate with the scrambled eggs and tomato, placing a muffin half on the side.

Hint: If you want the eggs to cook faster, you can keep the heat on medium-low.

Tip: If you don't want to waste yolks, try buying a carton of real egg whites.

Per serving: Calories: 158 Protein: 7 Carbs: 27 Sugar: 5 Fat: 2

Smoked Salmon with Hash Brown Cakes

SERVES 4 / PREP TIME: OVERNIGHT / COOK TIME: 10 MINUTES

This delightful breakfast dish will satisfy your craving for locks and bagels.

---

1 1/2 white potatoes, peeled
salt to taste
1/4 tsp paprika
1 tbsp golden flax meal
1 tbsp coconut oil
1 tsp olive oil
4 slices smoked salmon
2 tbsp capers

---

1. Boil the potatoes whole in salted water until soft, about 20 minutes.
2. Drain well and set aside to cool.
3. When the potatoes are cool enough to handle, grate them on the coarse side of a cheese grater into a mixing bowl.
4. Add to the grated potatoes the salt and pepper, the paprika, the flax meal, and the coconut oil.
5. Mix well with a large spoon.
6. Divide the potato mixture into 4 equal balls by hand.
7. On a plate, pat each ball into a flat round.
8. Leave plate covered in the fridge overnight.
9. When you're ready to cook the cakes, heat a non-stick frying pan over medium heat.
10. Add a drizzle of olive oil to the warm pan.
11. Gently fry the potato cakes 2 at a time.
12. Cook for 2 to 3 minutes on each side, or until they are light brown and heated through.
13. To serve, place 1 potato cake on each plate and top it with 1 slice of smoked salmon.
14. Sprinkle the capers over the salmon and serve.

Hint: Keep the potato cakes warm while you wait for the next batch to cook by placing them in a 200 degree oven.

Per serving: Calories: 215 Protein: 19g Carbs: 15g Fiber: 3g Sugar: 1g Fat: 9g

Homemade Gluten Free Everyday Bread

SERVES 8 / PREP TIME: 10 MINUTES / COOK TIME: 1 HOUR

Once you try this gluten free bread, it might just become your go-to bread recipe!

---

coconut oil as needed
1 1/2 cups rice flour
1/2 cup buckwheat flour
3 tsp baking powder
1/2 tsp salt

2 tbsp coconut sugar
2 egg whites
1 cup unsweetened light coconut milk
1/2 cup coconut oil
2 tbsp sesame seeds

---

1. Preheat the oven to 350 degrees.
2. Grease a loaf pan generously with coconut oil.
3. Sift together the rice flour, the buckwheat flour, the baking powder, and the salt into a large bowl.
4. Stir in the sugar.
5. Meanwhile, using an electric mixer, lightly beat the egg whites until they are just frothy.
6. Stir in the milk and the coconut oil.
7. Now pour the flour mixture into the bowl with the egg white mixture.
8. Beat on a medium speed for 2 to 3 minutes, or until smooth.
9. Pour this mixture into the greased loaf pan.
10. Smooth the top with a spatula.
11. Next, sprinkle the sesame seeds over the top of the mixture, pressing them down slightly.
12. Bake for 55 minutes to 1 hour, testing to see if a toothpick or knife comes out clean.
13. Set the pan to cool on a wire rack for at least 10 minutes.
14. Turn the bread out onto the wire rack to finish cooling.

Hint: You can substitute other gluten free flours in place of the rice flour if you'd like.

Per serving: Calories: 268   Protein: 6g Carbs: 37g Sugar: 3g Fat: 18g

Fresh Buckwheat Blinis with Scrambled Eggs and Smoked Salmon

SERVES 4 / PREP TIME: 10 MINUTES / COOK TIME: 15 MINUTES

This hearty yet classy breakfast will satisfy the whole family!

3/8 cup buckwheat flour
1 tsp baking powder
salt and pepper to taste
5/8 cup unsweetened rice milk
1 tbsp chopped green onions (green tips only)
2 egg whites

2 tsp coconut oil
4 large egg whites
To serve
2 tbsp capers
9 oz smoked salmon, sliced
4 wedges of fresh lime

1. For the blini batter, mix together the buckwheat flour, baking powder, salt and pepper, and rice milk to make a smooth batter.
2. Sprinkle in the green onions and mix until well combined.
3. In a separate bowl, whisk the first 2 egg whites with a pinch of salt until soft peaks form.
4. Gradually fold the whisked egg whites into the blini batter using a metal spoon.
5. Meanwhile, drizzle a small amount of the coconut oil into a frying pan over medium high heat.
6. Spoon large tablespoons of the batter into the pan to make medium sized pancakes, about 4 inches in diameter.
7. Cook the blinis in batches for 2-3 minutes on the first side and 1-2 minutes on the other side, or until golden brown.
8. Repeat until all of the mixture is used up.
9. Keep the finished blinis warm by placing them on a tray in a 200-degree oven.
10. For the scrambled eggs, whisk the remaining egg whites in a bowl.
11. Drizzle the rest of the coconut oil into the frying pan.
12. Pour in the eggs and constantly stir with a spatula to cook and scramble the eggs.
13. To serve, place two blinis onto each of four plates, spoon on the scrambled eggs, and sprinkle on a few capers.
14. Arrange the smoked salmon on the top and add the lime wedges.

Hint: Flip the blini pancakes when small bubbles appear on the surface and the underside looks cooked when you lift up the edge.

Per serving: Calories: 268 Protein: 24g Carbs: 20g Sugar: 1g Fat: 11g

Blueberry Breakfast Coffee Cake

SERVES 6 / PREP TIME: 3 HOURS TO CHILL / COOK TIME: 55 MINUTES

This delicious yet healthy breakfast cake is perfect for mid-morning brunch!

---

1 tbsp coconut oil
6 slices gluten free bread
1/2 cup organic blueberries (fresh or frozen)
8 large egg whites
1 1/8 cup unsweetened rice milk
1 tsp ground ginger

1 tsp vanilla extract
1/4 cup coconut sugar
1/4 cup coconut sugar
3 tbsp rice flour
1/2 tsp ground ginger
1 tbsp pure maple syrup

---

1. Grease a 9x13 baking dish with the coconut oil.
2. Cut the bread into 1 inch cubes.
3. Spread the cubes evenly over the bottom of the dish.
4. Sprinkle the blueberries over the bread.
5. Set aside.
6. Meanwhile, in a large bowl, whisk the egg whites, rice milk, ginger, vanilla extract, and 1/4 cup coconut sugar together until no lumps remain.
7. Pour this mixture evenly over the bread and blueberries.
8. Wrap the dish tightly with plastic wrap, or cover it with a lid, and refrigerate it for at least 3 hours, or overnight.
9. When you're ready to bake, preheat the oven to 350 degrees.
10. Remove the dish from the refrigerator.
11. Prepare the brown sugar topping by whisking together the coconut sugar, rice flour, and ginger in a medium bowl until there are no lumps.
12. Sprinkle this topping evenly over the top of the bread.
13. Place the dish in the middle of the oven and bake for 45-55 minutes, or until golden brown on top.
14. If you want the top to get crunchy, place the dish under the broiler on high for 2 to 3 minutes after it is done baking.
15. Drizzle a little maple syrup over each serving.
16. Cover any leftovers and refrigerate for up to 4 days.

Hint: You can add other toppings such as fresh fruit.

Per serving: Calories: 248 Protein: 10g Carbs: 46g Sugar: 22g Fat: 5g

Chocolate Oat Gluten Free Waffles

SERVES 4 / PREP TIME: 20 MINUTES / COOK TIME: 15 MINUTES

These delicious waffles will satisfy your craving for a breakfast treat anytime.

---

1 1/4 cup unsweetened light coconut milk
1 tbsp apple cider vinegar
1/4 cup melted coconut oil
2 tbsp pure maple syrup
1 tsp vanilla extract
1/4 cup steel cut oats (gluten free)
2 tbsp flaxseeds
3/4 cup rice flour

1/2 cup potato starch
3 tsp baking cocoa powder
1/2 tsp salt
1 1/2 tsp baking powder
1/2 tsp ground ginger
2 tbsp coconut sugar

---

1. In a mixing bowl, combine the milk and the vinegar and let this sit for a few minutes so it can activate.
2. Whisk the rest of the wet ingredients into this mixture: the melted coconut oil, maple syrup, and vanilla extract.
3. In another bowl, whisk together the dry ingredients.
4. Pour the wet ingredients into the dry ingredients.
5. Stir it all together with a big spoon until just combined. The batter will still be a little lumpy.
6. Let the batter rest for 10 minutes so the flour has time to soak up some of the moisture.
7. Plug in your waffle iron to preheat now.
8. Once 10 minutes has passed, give the batter one more swirl with your spoon.
9. Pour some batter onto the heated waffle iron, enough to cover the center and most of the central surface area, and close the lid.
10. Once the waffle is crisp, transfer it to a cooling rack or baking sheet.
11. Don't stack your waffles on top of each other, or they'll lose crispness.
12. Repeat with remaining batter.

Hint: If desired, keep your waffles warm by placing them on a rack in a 200 degree oven until you're ready to serve.

Per serving: Calories: 429 Protein: 5 Carbs: 59 Sugar: 13 Fat: 22

Nutty Cinnamon-Oat Granola Bars

SERVES 12 / PREP TIME: 10 MINUTES / COOK TIME: 40 MINUTES

These homemade granola bars are full of healthy fats to give you lots of energy.

1/2 cup coconut oil, melted
2 cups old fashioned rolled oats
1/2 cup sunflower seeds
1/4 cup sesame seeds
1/4 cup chopped pecans
3 tbsp pure maple syrup
1/2 cup coconut sugar
1 tsp ground ginger

---

1. Heat the oven to 325 degrees.
2. Grease a loaf baking pan with some of the coconut oil.
3. Mix together the oats, seeds, and nuts on a baking sheet.
4. Put the baking sheet in the oven for 5-10 mins to toast.
5. Meanwhile, pour the rest of the coconut oil, the maple syrup, and the coconut sugar in a medium sized saucepan.
6. Heat the oil mixture over low heat, stirring until the oil is melted.
7. Turn the burner off.
8. Add the oat mix and ginger to the saucepan.
9. Now mix everything together until all the oats are well coated.
10. Pour this mixture into the loaf pan.
11. Press down lightly.
12. Bake for 30 minutes.
13. Once it's done, take the pan out of the oven and let it cool on a wire rack.
14. Once it's cool, cut the loaf into 12 bars.

Per serving: Calories: 562 Protein: 15g Carbs: 34g Sugar: 13g Fat: 44g

Mediterranean Grilled Cheese and Tuna

SERVES 2 / PREP TIME: 5 MINUTES / COOK TIME: 5 MINUTES

These open sandwiches are the perfect lunchtime treat.

---

1 (5 oz) can chunk light tuna in water
1 tbsp chopped chives (green tips only)
2 tbsp olive oil
salt to taste
2 slices gluten free bread
1 large tomato, sliced

1/2 cup goat cheese, crumbled
1 pinch of paprika to serve

---

1. Turn on the broiler to high.
2. While the broiler is heating up, drain the tuna.
3. Flake the tuna into a medium bowl with a fork.
4. Add in the chives and olive oil.
5. Season with salt.
6. Meanwhile, toast the gluten free bread under the broiler until each slice is nicely browned on both sides, about 3 minutes total.
7. Remove the bread and spread the tuna mixture on top of each slice, right up to the edges of the toast.
8. Top each with a slice of tomato.
9. Sprinkle the cheese over the tomato.
10. Place the toast back under the broiler until the cheese is bubbling, about 1 minute.
11. Sprinkle each slice with a little paprika to serve.

Per serving: Calories: 342 Protein: 16 Carbs: 21 Sugar: 3 Fat: 22

Blueberry Orange Muffins

SERVES 12 / PREP TIME: 10 MINUTES /COOK TIME: 25 MINUTES

Satisfy your cravings for a breakfast treat with these fruity gluten free muffins.

1 1/4 cups gluten free all-purpose baking flour
2 tsp baking powder
3/4 cup unsalted coconut oil, softened
4 large egg whites
1 cup coconut sugar
3 tbsp cashew milk

½ cup carob powder
zest of 1 medium orange
1 1/2 cups organic blueberries

1. Heat oven to 350 degrees.
2. Line a 12-hole muffin tin with paper or foil muffin liners.
3. Pour all the ingredients except the fruit into a large bowl.
4. Beat the ingredients with an electric whisk on a medium speed until smooth.
5. Fold the fruit through the batter with a spatula by hand.
6. Fill each muffin paper about halfway.
7. Bake for 20-25 mins, or until golden and just firm.
8. Remove the muffins from the oven and allow to cool on a wire rack.

Hint: Allow about 30 minutes for the muffins to cool enough to peel the papers without destroying the muffin.

Per serving: Calories: 259 Protein: 3g Carbs: 37g Sugar: 23g Fat: 13g

Mediterranean Grilled Flat Bread

SERVES 1 / PREP TIME: 5 MINUTES / COOK TIME: 15 MINUTES

Be transported to the Middle East with this easy tomato and cheese lunchtime pita.

1 small zucchini, thinly sliced
2 tsp olive oil
1 dash dried basil
1 dash dried oregano
1 gluten free pita
1 roma tomato, sliced
1/4 cup mozzarella, grated

2 tbsp crumbled goat cheese
1 handful fresh basil leaves

1. Heat the oven to 425 degrees.
2. Meanwhile, place a frying pan over high heat on the stovetop.
3. Toss the zucchini slices in a small bowl with the olive oil, the dried basil, and the oregano.
4. Lay the zucchini slices in the frying pan and cook for a few minutes on each side, or until tender.
5. Place the gluten free pita on a baking sheet.
6. Cover the pita with tomato slices.
7. Arrange the zucchini slices on top of the tomatoes.
8. Sprinkle the mozzarella and goat cheese over the tomatoes.
9. Place the pita in the oven and bake for 8 minutes, or until the cheese has melted and the pita's edges are crisp.
10. Garnish with a few basil leaves to serve.

Per serving: Calories: 404 Protein: 20g Carbs: 68g Sugar: 7g Fat: 24g

Quinoa Breakfast Falafel

SERVES 4 / PREP TIME: 10 MINUTES / COOK TIME: 30 MINUTES

This gluten-free version of the Middle Eastern classic is sure to delight your tastebuds.

1 cup quinoa
2 1/4 cups low FODMAP vegetable stock, hot
3 cups fresh spinach, leaves roughly chopped
½ cup gluten free breadcrumbs

1 1/2 cups feta cheese, cubed
2 large egg whites, beaten
2 tbsp olive oil
romaine lettuce, to serve

1. Place the quinoa in a saucepan with the hot vegetable stock.
2. Simmer the quinoa for 18-20 mins over a gentle heat, or until the grains have fluffed up and the liquid has disappeared.
3. Remove from the heat.
4. Stir in the spinach with the quinoa and allow the pan to cool.
5. Once it has cooled down, pour the quinoa and spinach into a medium bowl.
6. Add the breadcrumbs, the feta, and the egg whites, stirring thoroughly.
7. Set this mixture aside.
8. Meanwhile, gently heat the olive oil in a shallow frying pan.
9. Using your hands, form the quinoa mixture into 8 round patties.
10. Add these patties to the frying pan and fry for 4-5 minutes on each side, or until each one is crisp and golden.
11. Serve on a bed of romaine lettuce.

Hint: Stuff the falafel into a gluten free pita with the lettuce rather than on a plate for a more Middle Eastern feel.

Per serving: Calories: 462 Protein: 20 Carbs: 41 Fiber: 5 Sugar: 5 Fat: 24 (Unsaturated: 12 Saturated: 11)

Mashed Potato Pancakes

SERVES 4 / PREP TIME: 10 MINUTES / COOK TIME: 30 MINUTES

Creamy mashed potatoes are transformed into crunchy cakes in this simple reci-

water to cover potatoes
2 small potatoes, peeled
4 tsp unsweetened rice milk
1 oz potato flakes
3 egg whites
1 tbsp goat milk

salt to taste
1 dash paprika
coconut oil, for frying

1. Place the potatoes in a saucepan.
2. Fill the pan with water, enough to submerge the potatoes.
3. Bring the water to a boil over high heat.
4. Boil the potatoes until they are soft all the way through, about 20 minutes.
5. When they are done, drain the potatoes well and return them to the pan.
6. Add the rice milk.
7. Mash the potatoes well with a masher or big fork.
8. Stir in the potato flakes.
9. Gradually add the egg whites.
10. Now stir in the goat milk.
11. Next, season the potatoes with the salt, and paprika.
12. Warm a frying pan over medium heat and grease it with a little coconut oil.
13. When the oil is hot, pour a ladle of the potato mixture into the pan and cook for 5 minutes, or until golden around the edges.
14. Turn over the potato cake and cook for another 3 minutes, or until golden-brown.
15. Repeat with the remaining potato mixture.

Per serving: Calories: 139 Protein: 6g Carbs: 21 Sugar: 1g Fat: 4g

Gluten Free Savory Chicken Crepes

SERVES 4 / PREP TIME: 10 MINUTES / COOK TIME: 40 MINUTES

This classic French dish comes to life with this delicious savory chicken filling.

---

2 tbsp olive oil
2 chicken breasts
3 tbsp buckwheat flour
1 1/2 unsweetened light coconut milk
1 handful fresh parsley, chopped
1 cup rice flour

1/2 tsp sea salt
4 large egg whites, plus one egg white beaten, for brushing
½ cup rice milk
1/3 cup gluten free breadcrumbs
1/2 cup lettuce, to serve

---

1. Heat 1 tbsp oil in a large frying pan and cook the chicken breasts for 5-8 minutes on each side, or until golden brown and cooked through. Set to one side.
2. In the same pan, stir in the buckwheat flour.
3. Now pour in the coconut milk, a little at a time, whisking continuously until you have a smooth sauce and allow to bubble for 2-3 minutes, or until thick.
4. Meanwhile, chop the chicken into pieces and add back to the pan along with any juices from the plate.
5. Stir in the parsley, turn off the heat and set aside.
6. To make the crepes, pour the rice flour into a large bowl and whisk in the salt.
7. Make a well in the centre of the flour and pour in 2 egg whites.
8. Pour the rice milk over the flour and egg whites.
9. Now whisk the eggs and milk, working the flour into the liquid until you have a smooth, thin batter.
10. Heat a large non-stick frying pan or crêpe pan with a drizzle of oil.
11. When the pan is hot, pour in a ladle of the batter and quickly swirl the pan to spread it across the surface and cook for one or two minutes.
12. When the underside of the pancake is golden, flip it and cook it for 30 secs.
13. Transfer the crepe to a plate and make three more pancakes in the same way.
14. Heat oven to 400 degrees and line two cookie sheets with parchment paper.
15. Take one crepe and brush a circle of beaten egg around the edge.
16. Pile a quarter of the chicken mixture into the centre of the crepe.
17. Now fold the pancake over and press the edges together to make a calzone shape. Transfer crepes to the cookie sheet as you complete each one.
18. Brush the top of each closed crepe with egg.
19. Sprinkle the gluten free breadcrumbs over the crepes and bake for 20-25 mins, rotating the trays halfway through.
20. Serve on a plate with a side of lettuce.

Per serving: Calories: 407 Protein: 26g Carbs: 44g Sugar: 1g Fat: 15g

Italian Turkey Breakfast Patties

SERVES 2 / PREP TIME: 10 MINUTES / COOK TIME: 10 MINUTES

If you're craving a classic sausage patty, this turkey substitute packs enough zesty flavor to replace it.

1 lb ground turkey
4 oz feta cheese
2 tbsp fresh basil
2 tbsp fresh oregano
½ lemon, zest only
2 egg whites
salt to taste
2 tbsp rice flour
2 tbsp coconut oil
1/2 romaine lettuce to serve

1. For the patties, place all of the ingredients except the flour and oil in a food processor.
2. Pulse these ingredients until well combined.
3. Using damp hands, shape the mixture into two patties.
4. Now dust the patties with the flour.
5. Heat the coconut oil in a frying pan.
6. Fry the patties for 3-4 minutes on each side, or until golden-brown and cooked through.
7. Serve with a lettuce salad.

Per serving: Calories: 570 Protein: 63g Carbs: 13g Fiber: 2g Sugar: 3g Fat: 30g

Teatime Banana Bread

SERVES 8 / PREP TIME: 10 MINUTES / COOK TIME: 45 MINUTES

This naturally sweet bread is also perfect as an afternoon treat with tea.

---

1 large over-ripe banana
1 tbsp rice milk
1/4 cup coconut oil, softened
2/3 cup rice flour
1/3 cup coconut sugar
1/2 tsp baking soda
1/2 tsp baking powder

2 egg whites
1 dash vanilla extract

---

1. Preheat the oven to 325 degrees.
2. Grease or line a loaf baking pan with parchment paper.
3. Use a fork to mash the banana in a medium mixing bowl.
4. Add the remaining ingredients.
5. Beat the batter with an electric whisk until it is combined and smooth.
6. Spoon the mixture into the prepared loaf tin.
7. Level the top of the batter with a spoon or rubber spatula.
8. Bake for 40-45 minutes, or until the bread has risen, is shrinking away from the sides of the pan, and golden brown.
9. Set aside the bread to cool for 10 minutes.
10. Remove the banana bread from the pan and leave to cool on a wire rack.
11. Slice and serve.

Per serving: Calories: 137   Protein: 1g Carbs: 21g Sugar: 9g Fat: 6g

Carrot and Banana Breakfast Bars

SERVES 8 / PREP TIME: 10 MINUTES / COOK TIME: 45 MINUTES

This easy baked breakfast treat makes the perfect grab-and-go morning meal.

1 ripe banana, peeled, pitted, and mashed
3 tbsp pure maple syrup
1/4 cup coconut sugar
3 cups old fashioned rolled oats (gluten free)
2 medium carrots, grated
zest of 1 orange
1/3 cup pumpkin seeds

1. Heat the oven to 325 degrees.
2. Line an 8x8 square baking dish with parchment paper.
3. Mix together the banana, the maple syrup, and the coconut sugar until it is smooth.
4. Mix in the rolled oats, the carrots, the orange zest, and the pumpkin seeds.
5. Stir everything well.
6. Next, pack the batter into the prepared pan, pushing down firmly.
7. Bake for 40-45 minutes.
8. Let the loaf cool in the pan before slicing into 16 squares.

Per serving: Calories: 203 Protein: 6g Carbs: 38g Sugar: 13g Fat: 4g

Traditional Lemon Poppy Seed Muffins

SERVES 6 / PREP TIME: 10 MINUTES / COOK TIME: 25 MINUTES

This gluten and lactose free version of these classic muffins is a keeper!

---

1 cup rice flour
1 tsp baking powder
1/2 tsp baking soda
1 pinch of salt
Zest of 1 lemon
1/2 tbsp coconut oil, melted
1 egg white, room temperature
1/2 tsp vanilla extract
1/2 almond extract

1/4 cup pure maple syrup
1/4 cup cottage cheese
2 tbsp lemon juice
2 tbsp cashew milk
2 tbsp poppy seeds

---

1. Heat the oven to 350 degrees.
2. Mix together the rice flour, baking powder, baking soda, salt and lemon zest in medium a bowl.
3. In a separate bowl, whisk together the coconut oil, egg white, and vanilla extract.
4. Stir in the extracts, maple syrup, and the cottage cheese until you get a smooth mixture.
5. Now stir in the lemon juice.
6. Stir the flour mixture into the liquid mixture until everything is just combined.
7. Pour in the milk while stirring.
8. Fold in the poppy seeds.
9. Divide the batter into six muffin cups.
10. Bake them 20-25 minutes in the oven.
11. Leave the muffins to cool in the pan for 10 minutes.
12. Then take them out and leave them to cool again.

Hint: The muffins are done when a toothpick comes out clean. You can store the muffins for 5 days in the fridge or longer when you freeze them.

Per serving: Calories: 174 Protein: 4g Carbs: 33g Fiber: 1g Sugar: 10g Fat: 3g

Savory Mushroom and Cilantro Oatmeal

SERVES 2 / PREP TIME: 5 MINUTES / COOK TIME: 10 MINUTES

A savory take on a classic breakfast - great if you don't have a sweet tooth!

1 cup unsweetened light coconut milk
1/4 cup steel cut oats (gluten-free)
1/4 cup mushrooms, sautéed
salt to taste
1/4 cup goat cheese, crumbled
1/2 tbsp fresh parsley
1 tsp fresh cilantro, loosely chopped

1. Pour the milk and the oats together into a small pan.
2. Bring the oats and milk to a boil.
3. Leave the oatmeal to simmer on low heat for 1-3 minutes, stirring now and then.
4. Stir the mushrooms into the oatmeal.
5. Leave the pan to warm up for a few minutes.
6. Season with salt.
7. Put the savory oats into two bowls and crumble the goat cheese on top of each.
8. Finish with some fresh parsley and cilantro.

Per serving: Calories: 163 Protein: 6g Carbs: 10g Sugar: 1g Fat: 12g

SEAFOOD

Shrimp Kebabs

SERVES 3 / PREP TIME: 10 MINUTES / COOK TIME: 10 MINUTES

Chunky grilled shrimp.

12oz shrimp, shelled
1 green bell pepper, roughly chopped
1 tsp dried oregano
1 tbsp garlic infused olive oil, divided
3 tbsp fresh lemon juice
A pinch of salt and pepper
2 tbsp water

---

1. In a bowl stir together the shrimp, oregano, and 1/2 tbsp. olive oil, and marinate for as long as you've got.
2. Add remaining olive oil, lemon juice, salt and pepper.
3. Thread shrimp and green pepper pieces onto metal skewers and grill over medium-high heat in grill pan just for 2 minutes per side or until cooked through.
4. Serve with the olive oil and lemon dressing.

Per serving: Calories: 199 Protein: 29g Carbs: 4g Fiber: 1g Sugar: 1g Fat: 7g

Clam Chowder

SERVES 6 / PREP TIME: 20 MINUTES / COOK TIME: 1 HOUR

A traditional home made dish.

---

1 tbsp olive oil
2 large carrots, peeled and diced
1/2 cup rice flour
2 cups low fodmap seafood stock
2 cups rice/soy milk
12 oz clams, shucked and chopped
1/2 tsp white pepper

1 tbsp dried parsley
A pinch of salt and pepper
1 bay leaf
12 small potatoes, peeled and diced into 1 inch cubes

---

1. In a large stockpot heat the oil over a medium heat. Add the carrots and sauté for 5 minutes.
2. Gradually sift in the flour, stirring thoroughly and scraping the bottom of the pan.
3. Next slowly stir in the fish broth, making sure there are no lumps.
4. Stir in rice milk until mixture is smooth.
5. Add the clams and spices, bring soup to a boil, then cover and reduce heat. Simmer for 30 minutes.
6. Add diced potatoes, cover and simmer for an additional 30 minutes.
7. Season with salt and pepper to taste.

Per serving: Calories: 221 Protein: 11g Carbs: 36g Fiber: 3g Sugar: 5g Fat: 4g

Thai Rice Noodle Salad

SERVES 3 / PREP TIME: 5 MINUTES / COOK TIME: 10 MINUTES

Fresh ingredients and a crisp taste.

Dressing:
2 tbsp fish sauce
1 tbsp white vinegar
2 tbsp fresh lime juice
1 tbsp garlic infused oil
8oz shrimp, shelled and deveined
1 cup flat, 1/4 inch dry rice noodles

1/4 cup peeled, diced, seeded cucumber
1/4 cup scallions, sliced
1 tbsp fresh cilantro leaves, finely chopped
1 tbsp fresh mint leaves, finely chopped
1/4 cup pineapple, diced (canned or fresh)

1. In a large stockpot heat the oil over a medium heat. Add the carrots and sauté for 5 minutes.
2. Gradually sift in the flour, stirring thoroughly and scraping the bottom of the pan.
3. Next slowly stir in the fish broth, making sure there are no lumps.
4. Stir in rice milk until mixture is smooth.
5. Add the clams and spices, bring soup to a boil, then cover and reduce heat. Simmer for 30 minutes.
6. Add diced potatoes, cover and simmer for an additional 30 minutes.
7. Season with salt and pepper to taste.

Per serving: Calories: 409 Protein: 17g Carbs: 69g Fiber: 4g Sugar: 3g Fat: 6g

Classic Calamari and Tilapia Paella

SERVES 4 / PREP TIME: 10 MINUTES / COOK TIME: 1 HOUR

This scrumptious blend of seafood is sure to please anyone craving paella!

3 tbsp garlic-infused olive oil
7 oz calamari (squid), cut into round
strips
2 cups water
1 cup dry white wine
1 cup brown rice
1 (6 oz) tilapia fillet, cut into big
squares
1 pinch of salt
2 tbsp turmeric
½ cup freshly chopped parsley (plus
more to sprinkle on top)
4 oz of cooked chicken breast, cut into
small pieces

1. Heat the olive oil in a large, deep pan over medium-high heat.
2. To the warm pan, add the calamari and cook for 5-10 minutes, or until the squid turns white or pink.
3. Stir the calamari frequently while cooking.
4. Next, add in the water and the wine and bring it to a boil.
5. Let this cook for 30 minutes over medium heat.
6. Now add the rice, tilapia, salt, turmeric, parsley, and chicken breast.
7. Bring all of this to a boil, then reduce the heat to low.
8. Simmer this pot for 30 minutes, or until the water is almost absorbed and the rice is tender.
9. Remove from the heat and serve with freshly chopped parsley sprinkled on top.

Per serving: Calories: 426 Protein: 28g Carbs: 36g Fiber: 3g Sugar: 1g Fat: 14g

Tuna, Carrot and Zucchini Fritters

SERVES 3 / PREP TIME: 10 MINUTES / COOK TIME: 10 MINUTES

These lightly fried bites are tasty and satisfying.

1/2 medium zucchini, grated
½ (5 oz) can tuna
1 medium potato, peeled, boiled and cubed
1/2 medium carrot, peeled and grated
¼ cup chives (green tops only), chopped

1 tbsp capers
salt to taste
1/4 tsp lemon pepper
1 tbsp brown rice flour
1 egg white
3 tbsp coconut oil

---

1. Grate the zucchini in a colander over the sink.
2. Press on the zucchini in the colander to drain the water.
3. In a large bowl, combine the tuna, potatoes, grated carrot, zucchini, chives, capers, salt, and lemon pepper, and gently mix.
4. Add the flour and egg, combining it all together.
5. Heat the coconut oil in a large skillet over medium high heat.
6. Scoop a big tablespoon of batter into the oil for each fritter.
7. Flatten the batter with a spatula.
8. Cook and flip until all sides are nice and golden brown, about 2 minutes for each side.
9. Serve immediately.

Per serving: Calories: 235 Protein: 12g Carbs: 16g Fiber: 2g Sugar: 2g Fat: 14g

Savory Fish and Potato Winter Stew

SERVES 3 / PREP TIME: 10 MINUTES / COOK TIME: 50 MINUTES

This delicious stew is the perfect way to stay warm on a cold evening.

---

4 tbsp coconut oil
1 bay leaf
3 medium potatoes, peeled and sliced into half-inch thick slices
1 red bell pepper, seeded and sliced
2 large tomatoes, diced
1 lb cod fillet, cut into strips
1 cup water

1 cup dry white wine
3 tbsp fresh oregano, chopped
1 pinch sea salt
1 pinch dried parsley
1 tsp turmeric
1/2 tsp paprika

---

1. Heat the coconut oil and the bay leaf in a large deep pan over medium-high heat.
2. Reduce the heat to medium.
3. Add a layer of potatoes, a second layer of bell peppers, and a third layer of tomatoes.
4. Lay the cod strips on top.
5. Add the water and the wine so you can bring it to a boil.
6. As it is coming to a boil, sprinkle the stew with the oregano, sea salt, parsley, turmeric, and paprika.
7. Simmer the stew for 40 minutes, or until potatoes are done.
8. Remove from the heat and serve in bowls.

Per serving: Calories: 523 Protein: 27g Carbs: 47g Fiber: 7g Sugar: 7g Fat: 19g

Quinoa Tuna Sandwich Spread

SERVES 4 / PREP TIME: 10 MINUTES / COOK TIME: 10 MINUTES

If you like quinoa and tuna, this hearty tuna spread is perfect for lunch any day.

2 cups water
1 cup quinoa
pinch of sea salt
1 cup fresh or frozen spinach
¼ cup chives (green tips only)
3 (5 oz) cans light tuna in water
1 tbsp lemon juice
1 tbsp lime juice

1 pinch sea salt
1 tbsp olive oil

1. Bring the water to a boil.
2. Add the quinoa and a pinch of salt to the boiling water.
3. Cook the quinoa for 10 minutes.
4. Add the spinach and reduce the heat to low.
5. When the water is gone, turn off the heat.
6. Fluff the quinoa and spinach with a fork.
7. Meanwhile, mix the chives with the tuna.
8. Now combine the quinoa and spinach with the chives, tuna, lemon juice, lime juice, salt, and olive oil.
9. To serve, spread over a gluten free cracker or a piece of gluten free toast.

Per serving (spread only): Calories: 258 Protein: 22g Carbs: 28g Fiber: 4g Sugar: 1g Fat: 7g

Lime and Parsley Encrusted Cod

SERVES 2 / PREP TIME: 10 MINUTES / COOK TIME: 25 MINUTES

This encrusted cod makes the perfect light summer dish.

---

2 (6 oz) cod fillets
1/2 slice gluten free bread, toasted and
crumbled into breadcrumbs
3 tbsp fresh parsley, finely chopped
1 tbsp garlic infused olive oil
zest of 1/2 lime
1 squeeze of lime juice
salt and pepper to taste
lime wedges to serve

---

1. Heat the oven to 425 degrees.
2. On a cutting board, season the cod with salt and pepper, to taste.
3. In a bowl, mix the breadcrumbs together with the parsley, garlic infused oil, lime zest, lime juice, salt, and pepper.
4. Mix thoroughly with your fingers.
5. Place the cod in a shallow, ovenproof dish.
6. Pour the seasoned crumbs over the cod and press the crumbs firmly onto the cod to form an even crust on both sides.
7. Bake for 20-25 minutes, or until the crust is browned and the fish is flaky and white.
8. Serve immediately, with lime wedges on the side.

Per serving: Calories: 191 Protein: 25g Carbs: 4g Fiber: 1g Sugar: 0g Fat: 8g

Lemon and Oat Crusted Salmon

SERVES 2 / PREP TIME: 15 MINUTES / COOK TIME: 15 MINUTES

This quick recipe will have you dining on rich-flavored salmon in 10 minutes!

2 large egg whites
1 1/2 cups quick-cooking oats (gluten-free)
1 tsp paprika
2 (6 oz) fresh salmon fillets
2 tbsp coconut oil
salt to taste
2 lemon wedges

1. Whisk the egg whites in shallow dish.
2. Combine the oats and the paprika in a medium bowl.
3. Now dip the salmon fillets into the egg whites, coating both sides.
4. Then dip the salmon into the oat mixture.
5. Press the oats gently into both sides of the salmon to form a sturdy crust.
6. Place the coated fillets on greased baking sheet.
7. Once you have finished coating the salmon, discard the oat mixture to prevent contamination.
8. Heat the coconut oil in a large, nonstick skillet over medium-high heat.
9. Add the fillets to the oil once it is hot.
10. Cook the salmon for 4 to 5 minutes on each side, or until it flakes easily when tested with a fork.
11. Season the salmon with salt to taste.
12. Serve each fillet with a wedge of lemon.

Hint: To further prevent sticking, lay a sheet of parchment paper down instead of greasing the baking sheet.

Per serving: Calories: 595 Protein: 45g Carbs: 42g Fiber: 7g Sugar: 1g Fat: 27g

Spicy Oriental Cod Cakes

SERVES 2 / PREP TIME: 10 MINUTES / COOK TIME: 15 MINUTES

Deliciously fragrant fishcakes.

---

1 (12 oz) cod fillet, cooked and shredded
1 egg white
1 tsp minced lemongrass
½ tsp minced ginger
1 tsp oyster sauce
1 tsp chopped fresh cilantro

2 tsp fresh parsley, loosely chopped
coconut oil for frying
lime wedges to serve

---

1. Place the cod in the bowl of a food processor or blender with the egg white.
2. Process until the cod and egg white are roughly combined.
3. Transfer this mixture to a large bowl.
4. To the bowl, add the minced lemongrass, ginger, oyster sauce, cilantro, and parsley.
5. Mix everything together until well combined.
6. Using damp hands, roll the mixture into balls the size of a tablespoon.
7. Flatten each ball slightly.
8. Add enough coconut oil to a wok to reach a depth of 2 inches.
9. Heat the wok over medium high heat until a tiny piece of bread sizzles when you drop it in.
10. Add 5 or 6 cod cakes to the hot oil.
11. Cook each cake for 3 minutes, or until golden.
12. Use a slotted spoon to transfer the cakes to a plate lined with a paper towel.
13. Repeat in batches with the remaining fish cakes.
14. Serve the cakes with lime wedges.

Hint: You can also check that the oil is hot enough by dropping in one grain of rice. It will rise to the top and start cooking.

Per serving: Calories: 594 Protein: 26g Carbs: 2g Fiber: 0g Sugar: 1g Fat: 55g

Baked Lime Sea Bass

SERVES 4 / PREP TIME: 10 MINUTES / COOK TIME: 25 MINUTES

This easy yet tasty recipe will spice up any large white fish.

---

1 (3 lb) sea bass, gutted and cleaned
3 lemongrass stalks, cut diagonally into
2½ cm pieces
2 tbsp garlic infused olive oil
1 (1 inch) piece fresh ginger, peeled and
sliced

2 tbsp olive oil
2 limes
1 tsp sesame seeds

---

1. Preheat the oven to 400 degrees.
2. Wash the sea bass inside and out, and pat it dry with a paper towel.
3. Score lines across the fillet and through the skin 4-5 times on each side.
4. Now lay the fish on a large piece of oiled aluminum foil, (big enough to wrap up the fillet loosely).
5. Put the lemongrass, and ginger into a mortar with 1 tablespoon of the garlic oil.
6. Squeeze the juice of one of the limes into the mortar bowl.
7. Mash the ingredients in the mortar with a pestle just until everything is bruised.
8. Next, pour out half the pounded mixture over the fish.
9. Add the last of the garlic oil to the fish as well.
10. Rub everything in, making sure you push some mixture into the cuts.
11. Cut the second lime into quarters.
12. Push two pieces of the lime into the bass's cavity along with the remainder of the pounded mixture.
13. Squeeze the juice from the last two lime quarters over the fish.
14. Pull the sides of the foil up to create a loose packet.
15. Crimp the edges of the foil to seal it, making sure there is some space around the fish.
16. Bake for 25 minutes.
17. After baking, let it rest for about 5 minutes before opening the packet.

Hint: If you're taking it to a picnic, wrap the bass in another layer of foil the minute it's out of the oven.

Per serving: Calories: 416 Protein: 64g Carbs: 6g Sugar: 2g Fat: 14g

Lime Cod En Papilote

SERVES 4 / PREP TIME: 10 MINUTES / COOK TIME: 12 MINUTES

Individual foil packets create the perfect steaming environment in this take on "en papillote."

---

2 stalks lemongrass, peeled and
bruised
¼ cup chives (green tips only), sliced
2 tbsp chopped fresh cilantro
4 (6 oz) cod fillets
1 lime, juiced
1 tbsp fish sauce
salt and pepper to taste
2 tbsp olive oil

---

1. Preheat the oven to 425 degrees.
2. Place a large, ovenproof frying pan in the oven to preheat.
3. Place four large squares of aluminum foil on the work surface.
4. Place an equal amount of lemongrass, chives and cilantro on each piece of paper.
5. Place the fillets on top of each square.
6. Pour the lime juice and fish sauce over everything.
7. Season each fillet with salt and pepper to taste.
8. Finally, place half a tablespoon of oil on top of each fillet.
9. Fold the foil over to encase the ingredients, crimping the edges down to create a seal.
10. Make sure that there is room for steam to circulate in the foil packets.
11. Remove the heated frying pan from the oven.
12. Place the foil packets in the pan.
13. Put the pan in the oven for 12 minutes.
14. After baking, allow the packets to cool for about 5 minutes before opening them.

Hint: Instead of the frying pan, you could preheat a roasting pan in the oven.

Per serving: Calories: 183 Protein: 25g Carbs: 4g Fiber: 0g Sugar: 2g Fat: 7g

Classic Steamed Bass with Lime and Brown Rice

SERVES 4 / PREP TIME: 10 MINUTES / COOK TIME: 20 MINUTES

Sea bass gets a lime makeover in this tasty recipe..

---

1 cup Swiss chard
4 (5 oz) sea bass fillets
1 tbsp ginger, finely shredded
1 tbsp garlic infused olive oil
1 tsp rice wine
1 bunch green onions, finely shredded
(green part only)
2 tbsp fresh cilantro, chopped
2 cups brown rice, cooked to serve
1 lime, cut into wedges, to serve

---

1. Preheat the oven to 400 degrees.
2. Tear off a large rectangle of foil, big enough to make a large envelope.
3. On the foil, place the Swiss chard, the sea bass, the ginger, and the garlic oil.
4. Pour the rice wine over this.
5. Fold the foil over and seal the edges by crimping them.
6. Put it on a baking sheet.
7. Bake for 20 mins.
8. After it's done baking. open the parcel and scatter the green onions and cilantro over the fish.
9. Serve with brown rice and lime wedges on the side.

Per serving: Calories: 284 Protein: 31g Carbs: 25g Sugar: 1 Fat: 6g

Greek Tilapia Bream with Yellow Squash

SERVES 2 / PREP TIME: 10 MINUTES / COOK TIME: 20 MINUTES

This marinated delight is perfect any night of the week.

---

2 (6 oz) tilapia fillets
1 lemon, juiced
2 tbsp olive oil, plus extra for drizzling
1 tbsp capers
1 can (2oz) anchovies
2 large tomatoes, halved
salt to taste

1 tbsp fresh parsley, finely chopped
1 pinch dried oregano
1 tbsp fresh mint, finely chopped
2 small yellow squash
2 cups fresh spinach leaves

---

1. For the bream, place the tilapia fillets in a bowl.
2. Squeeze the lemon juice over the fish.
3. Leave this bowl to marinate for 30 minutes.
4. Meanwhile, preheat the oven to 400 degrees.
5. Heat 1 tbsp olive oil in a large frying pan over medium heat.
6. Add the capers and anchovies.
7. Cook for 5 minutes, or until the anchovies have dissolved.
8. Add in the tomatoes, squashing them slightly.
9. Season this with salt.
10. Cook for five minutes.
11. Now place the tilapia in an ovenproof dish.
12. Season it with salt.
13. Add in the parsley, the tomatoes, the juices from the pan, a drizzle of olive oil, and the oregano.
14. Cover it all with aluminum foil.
15. Bake this in the oven for 20 minutes, removing the foil halfway through cooking.
16. While the fish is baking, make the salad.
17. Whisk 1 tbsp olive oil with the mint in a small bowl and set aside.
18. Next, trim the ends of the squash.
19. With a potato peeler or mandolin, slice the squash lengthways into wafer-thin slices.
20. Add the squash slices to the dressing.
21. Mix it well.
22. Set the dressing aside to marinate for at least 10 minutes.
23. After it has marinated, mix the spinach with the squash.
24. Place the salad on dinner plates.
25. When the fish is cooked, let it rest for one minute.
26. Serve the fish alongside the salad.

Per serving: Calories: 308 Protein: 26g
Carbs: 14g Fiber: 4g Sugar: 8g Fat: 18g

Fresh Tuna and Salmon Ceviche

SERVES 4 / PREP TIME: 10 MINUTES / COOK TIME: NA CHILL TIME: 30 MINUTES

The fresh take on ceviche is sure to delight everyone.

1 (6 oz) skinless salmon fillet, flesh sliced as thinly as possible
1 (6 oz) skinless tuna fillet, flesh sliced as thinly as possible
5 limes, juiced and zested
4 tbsp olive oil
1 handful fresh cilantro leaves, loosely chopped

1 large seaweed paper, crushed and shredded, to serve
olive oil to serve
4 lime wedges to serve

1. Put the fish slices into a large, shallow serving bowl.
2. Mix gently, using your fingers.
3. Sprinkle the lime zest over the fish.
4. In a separate bowl, whisk together the lime juice and olive oil until well combined to make a marinade.
5. Pour the marinade over the fish.
6. Again, mix gently using your hands.
7. Cover the bowl with plastic wrap.
8. Chill the bowl in the fridge for at least 30 minutes.
9. When ready to serve, mix in the chopped cilantro.
10. To serve, place one egg ring into the center of each of four serving plates.
11. Spoon in enough ceviche to almost reach the top of the egg rings.
12. Top with the shreds of seaweed paper and a drizzle of olive oil.
13. Garnish the plate with a wedge of lime.
14. Carefully remove the egg rings before serving.

Per serving: Calories: 305 Protein: 22g Carbs: 14g Fiber: 1g Sugar: 3g Fat: 19g

Monk fish Medallions with Lemon Dressing

SERVES 4 / PREP TIME: 20 MINUTES / COOK TIME: 15 MINUTES

Marinated meaty fish makes this dish one to return to again and again.

---

4 (5 oz) boneless monkfish medallions
1 stalk lemongrass, bruised and finely chopped
4 fresh lime leaves, chopped
1 tsp fresh lemon thyme leaves, choppd
5 tbsp olive oil, plus extra for frying
salt to taste
2 lemons, zest only
2 tbsp coconut sugar
1/2 cup water

3 tbsp olive oil
2 tsp lemon juice
½ tsp coriander seeds, toasted and ground
½ tsp chopped green onions, green tips only
2 tbsp roughly chopped fresh cilantro
1 handful spinach to serve

---

1. Place the monkfish in a bowl with the lemongrass, lime leaves, lemon thyme leaves, olive oil, and salt.
2. Cover and chill for for as long as possible.
3. Meanwhile, make the lemon dressing.
4. Chop the strips of lemon zest into a small dice.
5. Throw the zest into a pan of boiling water.
6. Drain the boiling water off the zest once it has returned to a rolling boil.
7. In a small saucepan, pour in the blanched lemon zest, coconut sugar, and water.
8. Cook this sugar mixture for about 5 minutes.
9. Now drain the lemon zest.
10. In a medium bowl, mix the sweetened zest together with the remaining ingredients and 2 tablespoons of water.
11. About 20 mins before you're ready to eat, remove the monkfish from the marinade.
12. Lightly season it with salt and pepper.
13. Heat a drizzle of olive oil in a large non-stick frying pan over medium heat.
14. Fry the monkfish medallions for 4 minutes on each side, or until golden brown.
15. Remove the cooked medallions from the pan and allow them to rest in a warm place for 4 minutes.
16. To serve, gently warm the dressing, adding more water if needed.
17. Garnish with spinach.

Hint: Serve the monkfish on top of cooked brown rice to add to the meal.

Per serving: Calories: 376 Protein: 25g Carbs: 8g Sugar: 6g Fat: 29g

Moroccan Tilapia and Tomato Tagine

SERVES 6 / PREP TIME: 10 MINUTES / COOK TIME: 20 MINUTES

The delicious sweetness of Moroccan cooking is featured in this fun tilapia recipe.

1 tbsp olive oil
2 tsp grated fresh ginger
1 tsp ground cumin
1 tsp turmeric
1 cinnamon stick
1 (15 oz) can diced tomatoes
1 dash salt
1 cup water
1 lb (of 2 oz) tilapia fillets
2 tsp pure maple syrup
1 tbsp chopped green onions

salt to taste
1 squeeze lemon juice to serve

1. Heat the olive oil in a large frying pan over medium heat.
2. Add the ginger, cumin, turmeric, and cinnamon stick.
3. Cook the spices for two minutes, stirring regularly.
4. Now add the tomatoes, salt, and the water.
5. Cook, stirring frequently, for 10 minutes.
6. Add the tilapia and simmer for 5 minutes, or until the fish is almost cooked through and tender.
7. Add the maple syrup and green onions and cook 2-3 more minutes.
8. Next, season to taste with the salt pepper.
9. To serve, spoon out the tagine into bowls.
10. Give each bowl a squeeze of lemon juice to serve.

Hint: Traditional tagine is cooked in a tagine clay dish. You cn pick these up from homeware shops and add to the authenticity and taste of the meal if you can get hold of one!

Per serving: Calories: 117 Protein: 15g Carbs: 5g Fiber: 2g Sugar: 3g Fat: 5g

Oriental Shrimp Pasta

SERVES 4 / PREP TIME: 10 MINUTES / COOK TIME: 20 MINUTES

This brightly flavored rice noodle and shrimp dish will satisfy everyone's seafood cravings.

5 tbsp reduced sodium soy sauce
3 tbsp coconut sugar
3 tbsp fresh lime juice
2 tbsp rice vinegar
2 tsp sesame oil
2 cups carrots, sliced thinly
1 tbsp chopped fresh ginger
6 green onions, green parts only, sliced
cooking spray
5 oz fresh spinach leaves

1 1/4 lb medium raw shrimp, peeled and de-veined
1/4 tsp salt
water for cooking noodles
8 oz rice noodles

1. In a medium bowl, whisk together the soy sauce, the coconut sugar, the lime juice, and the rice vinegar.
2. Set this mixture aside.
3. Heat the sesame oil in a large skillet on medium-high heat.
4. Add the carrots and continue cooking until they are tender, about 4 minutes.
5. Add the ginger and about three-quarters of the chives and cook for 1 minute, stirring frequently.
6. Transfer the ginger and onions to a medium bowl.
7. Return the skillet to the stovetop and mist it with cooking spray over medium heat.
8. Add the spinach and cook until wilted, stirring frequently, 2 to 3 minutes.
9. Add this to the bowl with the carrot mixture.
10. Return the skillet to the stovetop and mist it with cooking spray over medium heat again.
11. Toss in the shrimp and salt to taste.
12. Cook, turning occasionally, until the shrimp are firm to the touch and opaque in the thickest part, or about 4 to 6 minutes.
13. Meanwhile, bring a large pot of water to a boil.
14. Add the rice noodles and cook, stirring frequently, until al dente, about 3 minutes then drain the water.
15. Give the soy sauce mixture a quick whisk.
16. Add the soy sauce to the noodles.
17. Heat the noodles and sauce to a simmer over medium high heat.
18. Reduce the heat to medium and add the carrot mixture.
19. Gently toss everything together until it is all combined and heated through. Stir in the shrimp.
20. Serve right away, garnishing with the remaining chives.

Per serving: Calories: 394 Protein: 24g
Carbs: 63g Fiber: 5g Sugar: 7g Fat: 4g

Lime Shrimp Fritters

SERVES 4 / PREP TIME: 20 MINUTES / COOK TIME: 20 MINUTES

These zesty fritters are even more tasty with the homemade lime dressing.

1 lb large raw shrimp, peeled, deveined
and rinsed
2 egg whites, beaten
2 tbsp chives, green part only, diced
2 tbsp lime juice
2 cups gluten free bread crumbs
1 lime, juiced and zested
1/8 teaspoon sea salt
2 tablespoons olive oil

1. In a food processor, pulse the shrimp to coarsely chop it.
2. Add the egg whites, chives and lime juice.
3. Pulse everything together to combine.
4. Add 1 cup of the bread crumbs, pulsing to combine.
5. Form the mixture into balls.
6. Roll the balls in the remaining 1 cup of bread crumbs.
7. Place the balls on a parchment-lined baking sheet.
8. Refrigerate the sheet for 10 minutes.
9. While the shrimp balls rest, whisk together 1 tbsp of the olive oil, lime juice, lime zest, and sea salt.
10. In a large non-stick pan, heat the rest of the olive oil over medium high heat until it shimmers.
11. Working in batches, fry the fritters until they are golden brown, or about 4 minutes per side.
12. Serve the fritters hot with the lime dressing.

Per serving: Calories: 584 Protein: 20g Carbs: 13g Fiber: 1g Sugar: 2g Fat: 50g

Grilled Sardines with Cilantro Brown Rice

SERVES 2 / PREP TIME: 30 MINUTES / COOK TIME: 20 MINUTES

This salty and satisfying little meal is sure to be a crowd pleaser!

1 tbsp low sodium soy sauce
1 lime, juiced
1 thumb-sized piece fresh ginger, grated
1 tsp garlic infused olive oil

1 tbsp pure maple syrup
10 oz fresh sardines
1 cup brown rice
¼ cup scallions, sliced, green tips only
1 tbsp. fresh cilantro, chopped

1. To make the marinade, mix together the soy sauce, lime juice, ginger, garlic oil, and maple syrup.
2. Pour the marinade over the sardines.
3. Cover the marinade and chill it for 30 minutes.
4. Preheat the broiler on high.
5. Place the sardines, skin-side up, on a baking sheet lined with parchment paper.
6. Broil the sardines for 5 minutes.
7. Turn and baste them with the remaining marinade.
8. Broil for 5 more minutes.
9. Meanwhile, cook the rice following the package instructions.
10. After it's cooked and drained, toss the rice with the scallions and cilantro.
11. Serve the spicy rice with the sardines.

Per serving: Calories: 381 Protein: 23g Carbs: 45g Fiber: 3g Sugar: 9g Fat: 12g

Danish Potato Salad with Herring

SERVES 4 / PREP TIME: 10 MINUTES / COOK TIME: 20 MINUTES

This traditional potato salad gets a twist with the addition of lime.

1/2 cup water
2 lemons, juice only
1/2 cup white wine
2 bay leaves
1 tbsp white wine vinegar
1 tsp salt
4 oz herring fillet
4 cooked new potatoes

1/2 cup mayonnaise
1 tbsp chopped fresh dill
1/2 lemon, juice only
salt to taste
3 sprigs fresh dill to serve
lemon wedges to serve

---

1. First, bring the water, lemon juice, white wine, bay leaves, white wine vinegar, and salt to a slow boil in a pan.
2. Turn down the heat to a gentle simmer.
3. Add the herring to the pan.
4. Poach it for about 12 minutes, or until cooked through.
5. For the potato salad, cut the cooked potatoes in half.
6. Place them into a large bowl.
7. In another bowl, combine the olive oil, dill, mustard, lemon juice, and salt.
8. Add this mixture to the bowl with the potatoes.
9. Stir to coat the potatoes.
10. Meanwhile, drain the fish.
11. Place the fillet on top of the potato salad to serve.
12. Garnish with more dill and the lemon wedges.

Per serving: Calories: 333 Protein: 7g Carbs: 19g Fiber: 2g Sugar: 2g Fat: 23g

Grilled Tomato Salad with Mackerel and Capers

SERVES 4 / PREP TIME: 20 MINUTES / COOK TIME: 15 MINUTES

This fast and simple salad is the perfect addition to any lunch.

---

4 large tomatoes, halved
1 tbsp capers, drained
1/2 cup feta cheese, crumbled
1 cup fresh spinach leaves, washed
15 oz canned mackerel, drained and
sauce reserved
1 tbsp olive oil
1 tbsp red wine vinegar
salt to taste

---

1. Preheat the broiler on high.
2. Place the halved tomatoes (skin side up) on a baking tray covered in parchment paper.
3. Broil for 5-10 minutes, or until lightly chargrilled.
4. After removing the tomatoes from the oven, sprinkle them with the olives, capers, and feta.
5. Meanwhile, divide the spinach among 4 plates.
6. Roughly break up the mackerel and add it to the spinach already on the plates.
7. Place the tomato halves on top of the mackerel.
8. Then mix together the oil and vinegar in a small bowl.
9. Drizzle this over the tomatoes.
10. Sprinkle on salt to taste and serve.

Per serving: Calories: 261 Protein: 25g Carbs: 7g Fiber: 2g Sugar: 4 Fat: 15g

Ginger Tempura Shrimp

SERVES 2 / PREP TIME: 30 MINUTES / COOK TIME: 5 MINUTES

This classic dish has been transformed into a gluten free treat for any day of the

1 tsp finely chopped fresh ginger
1 tbsp coconut sugar
½ tbsp rice vinegar
1 cup water
1/2 cup rice flour
4 tbsp masa corn flour
1 pinch salt
1 cup club soda
10 large shrimp (peeled and butterflied)
coconut oil for deep frying

1. For the dip, heat the ginger, coconut sugar, rice vinegar, and water over medium heat for 10-15 minutes.
2. Remove the dip from the heat and set it aside until you are ready to use it.
3. To make the tempura, mix the rice flour, masa, salt, and pepper in a large bowl.
4. Gradually whisk in the club soda to form a smooth batter.
5. Set this aside for 20-30 minutes.
6. Meanwhile, heat the coconut oil in a deep-fat fryer to 350 degrees.
7. Dip the shrimp into the batter.
8. Deep fry each shrimp in the hot oil for 1-2 minutes, or until golden brown and cooked through.
9. Serve the fried shrimp alongside the ginger dip.

Hint: CAUTION: Hot oil can be dangerous. Do not leave the fryer unattended.

Per serving: Calories: 465 Protein: 8g Carbs: 45g Fiber: 2g Sugar: 2 Fat: 29g

Ginger and Parsley Salmon Patties

SERVES 4/ PREP TIME: 10 MINUTES / COOK TIME: 15 MINUTES

This recipe adds flavor and distinction to already delicious salmon patties..

---

4 (5 oz) boneless, skinless salmon fillets
1 thumb-sized piece fresh ginger, grated
1 lemon, juiced
¼ cup fresh parsley, chopped
salt to taste

1 tsp coconut oil
2 cups spinach leaves, washed
1 tbsp olive oil
1 cup cooked brown rice

---

1. Place the salmon in a food processor bowl with the ginger, half the lemon juice, the chopped parsley, and the salt.
2. Pulse until this mixture is roughly minced.
3. Shape the mixture into 4 patties.
4. Meanwhile, heat the oil in a non-stick frying pan.
5. Fry the patties for 4-5 minutes on each side, turning until crisp and cooked through.
6. Combine the spinach leaves with the olive oil and the rest of the lemon juice.
7. Serve the patties with the cooked rice and spinach salad.

Per serving: Calories: 305 Protein: 32g Carbs: 13g Fiber: 1g Sugar: 1g Fat: 13g

Gluten-Free Tomato Pasta with Tuna

SERVES 4 / PREP TIME: 5 MINUTES / COOK TIME: 25 MINUTES

This seafood take on an Italian classic brings spaghetti to a new level.

3 tbsp olive oil
3 tbsp fresh parsley, chopped
1 thumb-sized piece fresh ginger, grated
3 medium tomatoes, diced
1 (6.5 oz) can tuna in oil, drained and flaked

1 tbsp garlic infused olive oil
salt to taste
1 ½ cups rice spaghetti noodles

1. To prepare the sauce, heat the oil in a medium pan.
2. Toss in 2 tablespoons of the parsley and the ginger.
3. Fry these for a few minutes, or until they are slightly soft.
4. Add in the tomatoes and cook for another few minutes.
5. Fold in the tuna, garlic oil, and salt to taste.
6. Leave the sauce to simmer for 10 minutes.
7. Meanwhile, cook the rice spaghetti noodles for 8-10 minutes, or as directed on the packaging.
8. Drain the pasta and return it to the pan.
9. Pour the tuna sauce into the pasta and toss well.
10. To serve, sprinkle the remaining parsley over the pasta.
11. Divide it among four bowls.

Per serving: Calories: 528 Protein: 15g Carbs: 75g Fiber: 4g Sugar: 2g Fat: 18g

Pan Grilled Tuna Steaks with Fresh Basil and Quinoa

SERVES 4 / PREP TIME: 8 MINUTES / COOK TIME: 20 MINUTES

This refreshing combination of tuna, basil, and quinoa is sure to be a favorite!

1 1/2 cups water
1 cup quinoa
4 tbsp olive oil
1 tbsp red wine vinegar
2 tbsp finely chopped fresh basil
1 tsp smoked paprika
4 (5 oz) tuna steaks
4 tbsp olive oil
1 lemon, zested and juiced
1 tbsp fresh parsley, chopped
salt to taste

1. Bring the water to a boil in a pan over high heat.
2. Add the quinoa and lower the heat.
3. Cover and simmer the quinoa for 20 minutes, or until most of the water has been soaked up.
4. Turn off the heat and allow it to steam with the lid on.
5. Meanwhile, whisk 1 tbsp olive oil, vinegar, basil, and smoked paprika together in a small bowl.
6. Now place the tuna steaks in a medium bowl with the other 3 tablespoons of olive oil, the lemon zest, the lemon juice, the parsley, and the salt.
7. Heat a pan over a medium-high heat.
8. Add the tuna steaks and fry on each side for 2-3 minutes, or until cooked through.
9. To serve, drizzle the dressing over the grilled tuna and serve on a bed of quinoa.

Per serving: Calories: 276 Protein: 20g Carbs: 14g Fiber: 2g Sugar: 1g Fat: 15g

Baked Herb Salmon with Lime

SERVES 8 / PREP TIME: 20 MINUTES / COOK TIME: 60 MINUTES

This delightful take on baked salmon allows you to cook a big meal without a lot of fuss.

---

1 (4 1/2 lb) salmon fillet with skin on, filleted in half
3 limes, sliced
1/4 cup fresh parsley, chopped
2 tbsp fresh tarragon, chopped
2 bay leaves
2 tbsp chopped green onions (green tips only)
1 tbsp white wine

---

1. Preheat the oven to 400 degrees.
2. Place one of the salmon fillets, skin-side down, on a large sheet of foil or parchment paper.
3. Cover the salmon with the lime slices, herbs, and onions.
4. Lay the second fillet on top of the herbs and onions, skin-side up.
5. Tie the two fillets together with string in 2 or 3 places.
6. Splash the pair of fillets with the wine.
7. Fold up the foil or paper and crimp the edges to seal up the packet.
8. Place it on a baking sheet.
9. Bake the salmon for 50 minutes to 1 hour, or until the salmon is cooked through.
10. Check the salmon by poking a knife into the fillets and making sure the flesh flakes easily.
11. Serve the salmon in the foil or paper on a serving plate, or carefully lift out the fillets.
12. Slice the fish into portions and serve.

Per serving: Calories: 379 Protein: 55g Carbs: 3g Fiber: 1g Sugar: 1g Fat: 15g

Mint and Dill Baked Salmon

SERVES 4 / PREP TIME: 10 MINUTES / COOK TIME: 20 MINUTES

The olive and dill salsa verde on this salmon is delicious!

1/4 cup fresh dill, roughly chopped
1/4 cup fresh mint, roughly chopped
1/4 cup fresh parsley, roughly chopped
1/4 cup green onion, roughly chopped
2 tbsp capers
2 lemons, juice only
4 small salmon fillets, skin on
1 cup white basmati rice

---

1. Preheat the oven to 400 degrees.
2. To make the salsa verde, put the herbs, onions, capers, and the juice of 1½ of the lemons in a food processor.
3. Pulse until the mixture is roughly chopped.
4. Meanwhile, put the salmon fillets on a lightly oiled baking sheet.
5. Squeeze the juice of the remaining half lemon over the fish.
6. Bake the fish in the oven for 10-12 minutes, or until cooked through.
7. While the fish is baking, cook the rice according to the package instructions.
8. To serve, pile the salsa verde on top of the salmon fillets with the rice on the side.

Per serving: Calories: 282 Protein: 27g Carbs: 15g Fiber: 2g Sugar: 1 gFat: 13g

Fish Tacos

SERVES 4 / PREP TIME: 5 MINUTES / COOK TIME: 15 MINUTES

A lighter alternative to the usual beef tacos.

10oz skinless cod fillet, halved
½ tsp. ground cumin
A pinch of salt and pepper to taste
1 tbsp. garlic-infused olive oil
1 tbsp. olive oil
1 lime, juice and zest
4 rice tortillas
½ cup lettuce/spinach leaves, washed
¼ cup large beef tomatoes, diced

---

1. Season your fish with the cumin and the salt and pepper.
2. Set the fish to one side.
3. Heat the oil in a medium skillet over a medium heat.
4. Add the cod.
5. Cook each side for 5 minutes.
6. Meanwhile, use a small dish to mix together the olive oil, lime zest and juice.
7. You can heat up your tortillas in the microwave or in a lightly oiled skillet on the stove on low heat.
8. Once the fish is cooked, shred into bite size pieces.
9. Layer the tortillas with lettuce, tomato, fish, and then sprinkle in the cheese. Drizzle your lime dressing over your fish tortillas, roll and enjoy!

Per serving: Calories: 349 Protein: 26g Carbs: 27g Fiber: 4g Sugar: 3g Fat: 16g

Maple and Dill Salmon

SERVES 2 / PREP TIME: 5 MINUTES / COOK TIME: 20 MINUTES

A wonderfully sweet and savory baked fish recipe.

2x 5oz salmon fillets, skinless
A pinch of salt and pepper
1 tbsp maple syrup
1 lemon, halved
1 tbsp. dried dill

---

1. Combine the maple syrup, salt and pepper in a small bowl.
2. Marinade the salmon for as long as you can in this mixture.
3. Preheat oven to 400f/200c/gas mark 6 when ready to cook.
4. Line an oven tray with foil or parchment paper.
5. Squeeze half the lemon juice over the salmon and fold the foil/paper into a parcel with the lemon wedge inside.
6. Bake in the oven for a 15 to 20 minutes until thoroughly cooked through.
7. Remove from the oven and sprinkle over the dill.
8. Serve with your choice of salad, rice or vegetables.

Per serving: Calories: 246 Protein: 36g Carbs: 11g Fiber: 1g Sugar: 8 Fat: 6g

Coconut & Pineapple Shrimp Noodles

SERVES 2 / PREP TIME: 10 MINUTES / COOK TIME: 15 MINUTES

A delicious sweet & savory meal!

½ cup unsweetened desiccated coconut
2 egg whites
1 slice gluten free bread
12oz shrimp, peeled and deveined (de-frosted if frozen)
A pinch of salt

Pineapple Sauce:
¼ cup canned pineapple, diced
1 tbsp. garlic-infused olive oil

---

1. Preheat oven to 400f/200c/gas mark 6.
2. Line an oven tray with greaseproof parchment paper.
3. Make breadcrumbs out of the bread either with your fingers or in a blender.
4. Then, mix together the breads crumbs with the coconut and salt in a shallow dish.
5. In a small bowl whisk the egg whites.
6. Coat each shrimp into the egg whites followed by the coconut breadcrumbs.
7. Transfer each shrimp to the oven tray and bake in the oven for 5 minutes on each side.
8. Serve immediately once cooked through with a dip of your choice or on a bed of cooked noodles/rice.

Per serving: Calories: 535 Protein: 49g Carbs: 33g Fiber: 5g Sugar: 19 Fat: 23g

Lime Crab Cakes

SERVES 4 / PREP TIME: 10 MINUTES / COOK TIME: 20 MINUTES

So refreshing!

---

3 slices gluten free bread
16oz cooked crab meat
½ tsp. dried basil
½ tsp. dried oregano
½ tsp. marjoram
½ tsp. dried parsley
A pinch of salt and pepper
2 egg whites

---

1. Preheat oven to 400f/200c/gas mark 6.
2. Line an oven tray with greaseproof parchment paper.
3. Make breadcrumbs out of the bread either with your fingers or in a blender.
4. Mix the rest of the ingredients in a mixing bowl.
5. Slightly wet your hands and use your palms to shape 2 fishcakes.
6. Bake in the oven for 10 minutes on each side.
7. Serve with your choice of salad.

Per serving: Calories: 135 Protein: 24g Carbs: 10g Fiber: 1g Sugar: 1g Fat: 2g

Crayfish & Lemon

SERVES 2 / PREP TIME: 10 MINUTES / COOK TIME: 10 MINUTES

Deliciously simple!

---

2 lemons, juiced
1 tbsp. garlic-infused olive oil
1 tbsp. fresh parsley
A pinch of salt and pepper
2x crayfish/lobster tails

---

1. Preheat the broiler to a medium heat.
2. Whisk together the oil, lemon, parsley and salt and pepper (keep lemon wedges).
3. Place tails on an oven tray.
4. With a sharp knife or kitchen shears, carefully cut top side of shells lengthways.
5. Pull apart shells slightly, and season meat with the oil dressing.
6. Broil the tails 5 to 10 minutes or until meat is opaque.
7. Garnish with lemon wedges to serve.

Per serving: Calories: 121 Protein: 12g Carbs: 3g Fiber: 1g Sugar: 1g Fat: 7g

POULTRY

Turkey Vegetable Rice Soup

SERVES 4 / PREP TIME: 5 MINUTES / COOK TIME: 8 HOURS IN SLOW COOKER

A restoring recipe!

---

2 medium carrots, peeled and copped
1 medium zucchini, chopped
1/2 cup celery stalks, sliced
2 large potatoes, chopped
4x5oz boneless and skinless turkey
1 tsp olive oil
4 cups low FODMAP chicken stock
1 cup water

¾ cup brown rice
1 lemon, juiced
½ tsp dried thyme
A pinch of salt and pepper to taste
1 tbsp fresh cilantro/parsley

---

1. Except for the olive oil, add all of the ingredients into the slow cooker.
2. Cook on low for 7-8 hours or until the turkey is thoroughly cooked through.
3. Stir in the lemon juice and then turn off the slow cooker.
4. Ladle into individual bowls to serve and top with a sprinkle of fresh cilantro/ parsley.

Per serving: Calories: 224 Protein: 9g Carbs: 45g Fiber: 5g Sugar:4 Fat: 2g

Chicken Burgers & Pineapple

SERVES 2 / PREP TIME: 5 MINUTES / COOK TIME: 20 MINUTES

A delicious combination of lean meat burgers with zingy pineapple!

1 tbsp. canola oil
For the burgers:
10oz lean ground chicken breast (or turkey)
1 tbsp. dried dill
1 lemon, juiced
½ tsp dried thyme
A pinch of salt and pepper

For the salad:

½ cup canned pineapple, diced
¼ cucumber, diced
¼ cup salad lettuce (check individual tolerance with lettuce)
1 tbsp olive oil
A pinch of salt and pepper

1. In a large mixing bowl, combine all of the ingredients for the burgers and mix well.
2. Use slightly wet palms to form 2 burger patties.
3. Heat the canola oil in a skillet over a medium-high heat.
4. Add the burgers, cooking for 3-4 minutes before turning and allowing to cook on the other side for a further 8-10 minutes or until thoroughly cooked through (check with a knife in the center of each burger to ensure there is no pink meat and that juices run clear).
5. Now combine all of the salad ingredients in a salad bowl and toss to coat.
6. Serve each burger with a heap of salad and enjoy!

Hint: make up extra burgers and freeze in separate zip lock bags for 2-3 weeks – simply defrost before cooking thoroughly.

Per serving: Calories: 416 Protein: 43g Carbs: 10g Fiber: 2g Sugar: 6g Fat: 23g

Thai Spiced Chicken Noodle Broth

SERVES 4 / PREP TIME: 5 MINUTES / COOK TIME: 15 MINUTES

Our favorite pick-me-up with a little extra bounce!

2 cups water
2 cups low FODMAP chicken stock
8oz/1 cup gluten free noodles
10oz cooked chicken breast, skinless and boneless
½ cup celery, sliced
2 medium carrots, sliced
1 lime leaf

1 tsp dried basil
1 tsp dried cilantro
A pinch of salt and pepper to taste
1 cup bok choy
1 lime, juice and zest

1. Add the chicken broth and the water into a large pot over a high heat and bring to the boil, stirring frequently.
2. Lower the heat slightly and add the gluten free noodles, chicken and vegetables into the pot.
3. Reduce the heat down to low and bring to a simmer.
4. Add the herbs and salt and pepper as desired.
5. After 10 minutes add the bok choy leaves and lime juice.
6. Cook for 5 minutes or until leaves are slightly wilted.
7. Stir through the lime zest and ladle into soup bowls to serve.

Per serving: Calories: 244 Protein: 5g Carbs: 53g Fiber: 3g Sugar: 2g Fat: 1g

Loaded Potato Skins

SERVES 2 / PREP TIME: 5 MINUTES / COOK TIME: 50 MINUTES

These are a perfect dinner time meal for the whole family!

---

2 large white potatoes, sliced in half
1 tbsp. garlic-infused olive oil
A pinch of salt and pepper
4oz cooked chicken breast, skinless
and boneless
2 tbsp chives, chopped
1 red pepper, finely diced
2 tbsp goats cheese, crumbled

---

1. Preheat oven to 350f/180c/gas mark 4.
2. Then, place the potatoes in a casserole dish.
3. Drizzle the garlic infused olive oil on top of each half and season with salt and pepper.
4. Bake in the oven for 30-40 minutes or until skins are crispy and potato is fluffy and soft.
5. Remove from the oven and allow to cool.
6. Scoop out the potato from the inside and add to a mixing bowl.
7. Leave the skins to one side.
8. Add the chopped cooked chicken, diced pepper and chives to the potato and mix well.
9. Scoop back into the potato skins and place in the oven.
10. Cook for a further 10 minutes or until golden and sprinkle with goats cheese until bubbling and crispy.
11. Remove and serve with a side salad of your choice.

Per serving: Calories: 391 Protein: 26g Carbs: 34g Fiber: 4g Sugar: 4g Fat: 17g

Lemon & Cilantro Chicken Salad

SERVES 2 / PREP TIME: 5 MINUTES / COOK TIME: 25 MINUTES

A light summer dish or delicious side.

10oz skinless and boneless chicken breasts
1 tsp dried oregano
1 tsp dried thyme
1 lemon, juiced
1 tbsp olive oil
A pinch of salt and pepper

For the salad:
2 large tomatoes, sliced
½ cucumber, sliced
2 scallions stems, sliced (green tips only)

1 tbsp. fresh cilantro, chopped
2 cups spinach, washed (organic if possible)
1 tbsp olive oil
A pinch of salt and pepper

---

1. Preheat the broiler to a medium-high heat.
2. Butterfly each chicken breast and flatten.
3. Mix 1 tbsp. olive oil, juice of ½ lemon, dried herbs and a little salt and pepper.
4. Marinade the chicken for as long as possible or you can cook right away.
5. Add to a lined oven tray and broil for 10-12 minutes on each side.
6. Ensure chicken is cooked thoroughly by inserting a knife into the center – the juices should run clear and meat should be white.
7. Now combine the salad ingredients and toss to coat.
8. Slice the chicken breast and layer on top of the salad.
9. Sprinkle with a little more salt and pepper to serve.

Per serving: Calories: 395 Protein: 45g Carbs: 11g Fiber: 4g Sugar: 5g Fat: 19g

Teriyaki Meatballs

SERVES 2 / PREP TIME: 10 MINUTES / COOK TIME: 35 MINUTES

A little twist on the Italian favorite!

For the meatballs:
10oz lean ground turkey
1 egg white
1 tbsp gluten free bread crumbs (optional)
1 tsp dried rosemary
1 tbsp fresh ginger
2 scallion stems, sliced (green tips only)
1 tbsp reduced sodium soy sauce

1 tbsp canola oil
For the sauce:
¼ cup reduced sodium soy sauce
½ cup water
1 red bell pepper, diced
2 tsp brown sugar
1 tbsp cornstarch

---

1. Preheat oven to 350f/180c/gas mark 4.
2. Lightly oil an oven tray.
3. In a medium bowl mix together the ingredients for the meatballs.
4. Then, form 10 meatballs with the palms of your hands.
5. Place the meatballs on the oven tray.
6. Bake the meatballs for 20 minutes or until they are fully cooked through.
7. Stir together all of the ingredients for the sauce excluding the cornstarch.
8. In a pan over a medium heat add the sauce, stirring until mixed well and then lowering to a simmer.
9. Add your cooked meatballs to the sauce.
10. Cover and simmer in the sauce for 5 minutes.
11. Meanwhile stir 2 tbsp. water into the cornstarch in a separate small bowl.
12. Add this into the meatball sauce to thicken (this part is optional if corn does not agree with you – you could add 1 tbsp. rice flour at this stage instead to thicken).
13. Once the sauce is thick, serve right away over rice or noodles.

Per serving: Calories: 454 Protein: 43g Carbs: 19g Fiber: 2g Sugar: 8g Fat: 23g

Garlic Sautéed Chicken & Sunflower Sauce

SERVES 2 / PREP TIME: 5 MINUTES / COOK TIME: 1 HOUR

This easy one-pot meal is sure to please your guests with nut allergies.

---

3 tbsp garli-infused olive oil
4 chicken breasts, skinless
water to cover chicken
2/3 cup rice milk
2 tbsp sunflower butter
1 pinch of salt

---

1. Heat the olive oil in a large pot over medium-high heat.
2. Toss in the chicken and cook for 2-3 minutes, or until golden brown, turning often to ensure even color.
3. Cover the chicken with water and let it cook over medium-low heat for about 40 minutes, stirring occasionally.
4. In a separate bowl, whisk the milk and sunflower butter until well blended.
5. Add this mixture to the chicken and cook for about 20 minutes.
6. Give everything a good stir.
7. Salt this mixture to taste.
8. Remove from the heat and serve.

Hint: You may consider serving this with your favorite rice, such as jasmine rice.

Per serving: Calories: 323 Protein: 33g Carbs: 4g Fiber: 1g Sugar: 3g Fat: 19g

Minty Chicken Noodle Soup

SERVES 6 / PREP TIME: 10 MINUTES / COOK TIME: 40 MINUTES

This take on the classic cold day soup is refreshing and tasty!

½ cup fresh or frozen spinach, chopped
2 carrots, peeled and sliced
6 cups low FODMAP chicken broth
6 chicken breasts, baked
1 cup rice vermicelli noodles
1 pinch salt
1 tbsp fresh mint leaves, chopped

---

1. In a large pot, add the spinach, carrots, and the broth.
2. Bring this to a simmer over medium-high heat.
3. Turn down the heat slightly and allow it to simmer for about 30 minutes.
4. Meanwhile, shred the chicken with forks or meat claws.
5. To the broth, add the noodles, shredded chicken, and salt.
6. Cook for 7 minutes.
7. Ladle in to bowls and serve with the mint leaves.

Per serving: Calories: 371 Protein: 33g Carbs: 42g Fiber: 2g Sugar: 0g Fat: 6g

Indian Chicken and Rice

SERVES 3 / PREP TIME: 10 MINUTES / COOK TIME: 1 HOUR

This simple yet scrumptious chicken and rice dish will have you asking for more!

---

3 tbsp. garlic-infused olive oil
2 chicken breasts, skinless
1 tbsp turmeric
water to cover chicken
1 cup white rice
1 large carrot, finely chopped
sea salt

---

1. Heat the olive oil in a large non-stick frying pan over medium-high heat.
2. Remove the garlic clove once the oil has heated.
3. Toss in the chicken and turmeric and cook for 2–3 minutes, or until golden brown, turning often to ensure even color.
4. Cover the chicken with water and let it cook over medium heat for about 20 minutes, stirring occasionally.
5. Add the rice and carrot and cover again with water.
6. Bring to the soup to a boil.
7. Salt the soup to taste, then reduce the heat to low.
8. Cover and simmer the soup for another 15 minutes, or until all the water is absorbed and the rice is tender.
9. Give everything a good final stir before removing from the heat.
10. Let the dish stand, covered, for 15 minutes before serving.

Per serving: Calories: 477 Protein: 26g Carbs: 54g Fiber: 2g Sugar: 0g Fat: 1g

Gluten Free Turkey & Tomato Pasta

SERVES 4 / PREP TIME: 5 MINUTES / COOK TIME: 15 MINUTES

Delight a guest with this simple yet elegant pasta dish topped by a turkey breast.

---

2 (6 oz) turkey breasts
2 tbsp lemon juice
1 pinch salt
4 oz rice noodles
2 large tomatoes, quartered
¼ cup green onions (green tips only)
sliced
1 squeeze lime juice

¼ cup sesame seeds
salt to taste
1 tbsp olive oil to serve

---

1. Season the turkey with the lemon juice and the pinch of salt.
2. Sautee the turkey over medium heat for 3-5 minutes on each side, or until no longer pink.
3. Cut the turkey breasts in half.
4. Cook the noodles for 4 minutes in boiling water.
5. Drain the noodles under cold water.
6. Transfer them to a salad bowl.
7. Stir in the tomatoes, green onions, and lime juice.
8. Sprinkle the sesame seeds over the noodles.
9. Finally, season the noodles to taste with the salt, and olive oil.
10. Serve the turkey on a bed of noodles.

Per serving: Calories: 204 Protein: 11g Carbs: 28g Fiber: 3g Sugar: 2g Fat: 5g

Fresh Ginger Chicken Salad

SERVES 3 / PREP TIME: 10 MINUTES / COOK TIME: 30 MINUTES

This well-garnished and tasty salad will make you re-think salads for good!

5/8 cup coconut sugar
2/3 cup fresh lemon juice
1 inch piece fresh ginger, grated
5 lime leaves
1 lemongrass stalk, chopped
2 (5 oz) chicken breasts, cut into strips
1 carrot, peeled and grated
1 bunch bok choy, finely sliced
4 oz rice noodles, cooked
1/8 cup chopped fresh cilantro leaves

---

1. For the dressing, place the sugar, lemon juice, and ginger in a saucepan and bring to a boil, stirring until the sugar has dissolved.
2. Add the lime leaves, and lemongrass.
3. Return the mixture to a boil.
4. Remove the pan from the heat and let it cool.
5. When cool, strain the mixture through a fine mesh strainer and set aside.
6. Meanwhile, add the chicken to a parchment lined baking tray.
7. Place it under the broiler on medium heat for 15-20 minutes, or until completely cooked through.
8. Turn the chicken occasionally while it is broiling.
9. Meanwhile, mix the carrot, bok choy, and noodles together in a bowl.
10. Add the dressing and mix it all together until well combined.
11. Divide the salad between 2 serving bowls.
12. To serve, top the salad with the chicken pieces and sprinkle the cilantro on top.

Per serving: Calories: 434 Protein: 26g Carbs: 77g Fiber: 5g Sugar: 38g Fat: 3g

Roasted Herbed Chicken & Potatoes

SERVES 6 / PREP TIME: 10 MINUTES / COOK TIME: 40 MINUTES

This potato and chicken dish is sure to be a dinner winner!

---

3 cups red potatoes, thinly sliced
2 tbsp olive oil
6 chicken breasts, skin on
salt to taste
1 lemon, sliced into wedges

5 sprigs fresh thyme (or 2 tbsp dried)
1 cup white wine
1 cup low FODMAP chicken broth

---

1. Preheat the oven to 425 degrees.
2. Place the potatoes into a 9x13 glass baking dish.
3. Drizzle them with 1 tablespoon of the oil.
4. Season them well with the salt.
5. Toss to coat the potatoes.
6. Roast them for 20 minutes, or until they start to crisp.
7. Meanwhile, season the chicken breasts to taste with the salt.
8. Add them to the baking dish along with the lemon wedges and thyme.
9. Drizzle the chicken with the remaining oil.
10. Return the dish to the oven for 20 minutes.
11. Next, pour the wine and broth over the dish.
12. Roast for a final 20 minutes, or until the chicken is golden and cooked through.

Per serving: Calories: 476 Protein: 57g Carbs: 9g Fiber: 1g Sugar: 0g Fat: 19g

Herbed Shrimp and Chicken Risotto

SERVES 4 / PREP TIME: 5 MINUTES / COOK TIME: 50 MINUTES

Adding shrimp to this baked chicken and rice is a refreshing twist!

2 medium tomatoes, diced
1 tbsp olive oil
1 tbsp garlic infused olive oil
3/4 cup rice
4 skinless chicken breasts, halved
2 tsp chopped fresh rosemary
2 tsp chopped chives

4 cups low FODMAP chicken broth
salt to taste
8 large raw shrimp

1. Preheat the oven to 425 degrees.
2. Place the tomatoes in a baking dish.
3. Drizzle the garlic oil and olive oil over the tomatoes.
4. Roast them for 20 minutes, or until the tomatoes are softened.
5. Stir in the risotto rice, chicken, rosemary, chives, chicken broth, and some salt, mixing it all together very well.
6. Return the dish to the oven for 20 minutes.
7. Remove the dish and stir in the shrimp.
8. Return it to the oven for 10 more minutes, or until the rice is tender and the chicken and shrimp are cooked through.

Per serving: Calories: 322 Protein: 39g Carbs: 14g Fiber: 1g Sugar: 2 Fat: 12g

Lime Chicken Kebabs

SERVES 2 / PREP TIME: 30 MINUTES / COOK TIME: 55 MINUTES

This healthy take on the Mediterranean favorite is sure to please everyone!

2 tbsp olive oil
1 tsp crushed coriander seeds
1 tsp grated lime zest
½ tsp coconut sugar
1 tbsp garlic infused olive oil
2 (5 oz) chicken breasts, cubed
1 lime, cut into wedges
2 metal skewers

1. Preheat the oven to 375 degrees.
2. Mix together the ingredients for the marinade: the olive oil, the coriander seeds, the lime zest, the sugar, and the garlic oil.
3. Set the marinade aside.
4. Put the cubed chicken breasts in a glass baking dish.
5. Spoon the marinade over the chicken.
6. Next, squeeze a little lime juice over the top.
7. Cover and marinate for 30 minutes in the fridge.
8. When ready to cook, thread the marinated chicken onto the skewers.
9. Place each loaded skewer onto a baking sheet.
10. Roast the chicken skewers, uncovered, for 20-25 minutes.
11. To serve, push the meat off the skewers onto a platter.

Hint: To check if they are done, poke the chicken with your finger. If they are still a bit soft, bake the chicken a bit longer.

Per serving: Calories: 352 Protein: 31g Carbs: 2g Fiber: 1g Sugar: 1g Fat: 24g

Easy Orange Maple Chicken

SERVES 4 / PREP TIME: 10 MINUTES / COOK TIME: 20 MINUTES

This simple marinade transforms chicken breast into an entrée to remember.

---

4 (5 oz) skinless chicken breasts
3 tbsp pure maple syrup
1 orange, zest only
2 tbsp fresh orange juice
salt to taste

---

1. Score each chicken breast with a sharp knife.
2. Place the other ingredients into a wide, shallow bowl.
3. Swirl them together until everything is well mixed.
4. Add the chicken breasts to the mixture.
5. Turn them in the sauce until they are evenly coated.
6. Marinade for as long as possible in the fridge.
7. When ready to cook, preheat the broiler to low.
8. Broil the chicken for 10 minutes on each side.
9. Turn them once and baste on the marinade as you go.
10. Bake until the chicken is brown and glossy.

Per serving: Calories: 206 Protein: 31g Carbs: 11g Fiber: 0g Sugar: 11g Fat: 4g

Roasted Red Pepper Chicken

SERVES 4 / PREP TIME: 10 MINUTES / COOK TIME: 40 MINUTES

This zesty chicken is sure to be a crowd pleaser!

---

2 (5 oz) skinless chicken breasts
2 red bell peppers, deseeded and
sliced
1 tbsp garlic infused olive oil
1 tsp smoked paprika
3 tbsp olive oil
1 lemon, zested and juiced
2 tbsp fresh basil, chopped
2 tbsp fresh cilantro, chopped

---

1. Preheat the oven to 400 degrees.
2. Place the chicken and peppers in a large bowl.
3. In another bowl, mix together the garlic infused oil, paprika, olive oil, lemon zest, and lemon juice.
4. Pour this combination over the chicken and peppers.
5. Divide the mixture between 2 baking sheets.
6. Roast the chicken for 40 minutes, turning over halfway through.
7. Bake until the chicken is cooked through and the juices run clear.
8. Serve the chicken and peppers in bowls with freshly torn basil and cilantro.

Per serving: Calories: 223 Protein: 16g Carbs: 4g Fiber: 1g Sugar: 3g Fat: 15g

Classic Chicken Meatballs & Rice

SERVES 2 / PREP TIME: 10 MINUTES / COOK TIME: 20 MINUTES

A take on a Swedish favorite.

½ celery stalk, sliced
1 small carrot, peeled and sliced
2 (5 oz) skinless chicken breasts,
sliced
2 tbsp chives (green tips only)
coconut oil for greasing
1 cup cooked brown rice
salt to taste

---

1. Preheat the oven to 400 degrees.
2. Blend the celery, carrot, chicken, and chives in a food processor until it is finely chopped together.
3. Shape into small meatballs.
4. To cook, put on a baking tray lined with foil greased with the coconut oil.
5. Bake the meatballs for 20 minutes.
6. Turn over halfway through baking, after 10 minutes.
7. They are done when they are brown and cooked through.
8. Serve with brown rice seasoned with the salt and pepper.

Per serving: Calories: 344 Protein: 34g Carbs: 25g Fiber: 3g Sugar: 2g Fat: 1g

Chicken Salad & Patatas Bravas

SERVES 4 / PREP TIME: 10 MINUTES / COOK TIME: 40 MINUTES

This take on the classic dish will wow your taste buds!

---

2 baking potatoes, peeled and cubed
2 tbsp olive oil
2 tbsp smoked paprika
4 tsp balsamic vinegar
salt to taste
1 red bell pepper, seeded and diced

4 (5 oz) skinless boneless chicken breasts
2 cups fresh spinach

---

1. Preheat the oven to 400 degrees.
2. Spread the potatoes on a large baking sheet.
3. Mix 1 tablespoon of the oil with 1 tablespoon of the paprika, half the balsamic vinegar, and the salt.
4. Pour this mixture over the potatoes.
5. Toss the potatoes in the oil mixture until they are each coated.
6. Bake in the oven for 10 minutes.
7. Meanwhile, prepare the chicken.
8. Mix the pepper with the chicken in a small bowl.
9. Sprinkle the chicken with the paprika.
10. Spread the chicken and peppers on top of the potatoes.
11. Return the dish to the oven for 30 minutes, or until the chicken is cooked and the potatoes are crispy.
12. When the chicken is cooked, mix together the remaining oil and balsamic vinegar.
13. Drizzle this over the spinach.
14. Serve the chicken with the paprika potatoes and salad.

Per serving: Calories: 393 Protein: 36g Carbs: 37g Fiber: 6g Sugar: 4g Fat: 11g

Chicken & Tomato Stew

SERVES 4   PREP TIME: 10 MINUTES   COOK TIME: 45 MINUTES

A savory blend of tomatoes and parsley simmers with chicken breast in this hearty dish.

1 tbsp olive oil
4 (5 oz) skinless chicken breasts
1 stalk celery, finely chopped
1 medium carrot, peeled and finely diced
1 pinch salt
1 (15 oz) can diced tomatoes
1 cup low FODMAP chicken stock
1 tbsp tomato paste
1 tsp dried oregano

1 tbsp garlic infused olive oil
1 tbsp chopped parsley to serve
1 tsp coconut sugar
salt to taste
2 cups potatoes, cubed

1. Heat a large saucepan over medium heat.
2. Add the oil.
3. Once the oil is hot, add the chicken breasts to the pan.
4. Brown the chicken on each side for 3-4 minutes, or until golden brown.
5. Remove the chicken from the pan and set it to one side.
6. Add the celery and carrot with the pinch of salt to the saucepan.
7. Stir the vegetables over the heat for 6 minutes.
8. Add the browned chicken back to the pan along with any juices from the meat.
9. Over the chicken and vegetables, add the tomatoes, stock, paste, oregano, garlic oil, sugar, and parsley.
10. Mix this well to make sure everything is evenly distributed.
11. Next, season the pan with a little salt and pepper.
12. Cover it with a lid.
13. Gently simmer the pan for 20 minutes, or until the chicken is cooked through and the sauce is slightly thickened.
14. Meanwhile, boil the potatoes in a saucepan of boiling water for 10-12 minutes, or until tender and cooked through.
15. Drain the potatoes and serve it alongside the chicken and tomatoes.

Per serving: Calories: 324 Protein: 35g Carbs: 21g Fiber: 5g Sugar: 6g Fat: 11g

Sautéed Herby Greek Chicken

SERVES 2 / PREP TIME: 10 MINUTES / COOK TIME: 25 MINUTES

This lovely sautéed chicken dish carries the flavos of Greece with balsamic vine-

---

2 tbsp olive oil
2 boneless, skinless chicken breasts
1 cup tomatoes, diced
1 tbsp balsamic vinegar
6 pimiento-stuffed green olives, thickly
sliced
1 cup low FODMAP chicken stock
1 tbsp dried oregano
1 tsp dried parsley
1 tsp chopped green onion, green tips
only
1 tbsp garlic infused olive oil

---

1. Heat the oil in a large non-stick frying pan.
2. Fry the chicken, flat side down, for 6-8 mins.
3. Lift the chicken from the pan and set it aside.
4. To the pan, add the tomatoes with the balsamic vinegar, olives, stock, herbs, green onions, and the garlic oil.
5. Now simmer this pan, stirring frequently, for 7-8 minutes, or until pulpy.
6. Return the chicken and any juices to the pan and gently simmer, covered, for 5 minutes more, to finish cooking the chicken.
7. Serve on dinner plates.

Per serving: Calories: 387 Protein: 32g Carbs: 7g Fiber: 2g Sugar: 4g Fat: 26g

Red Pepper & Tomato Chicken

SERVES 2 / PREP TIME: 10 MINUTES / COOK TIME: 40 MINUTES

This easy baked chicken makes the perfect busy day evening meal.

---

1 cup small red potatoes, thinly sliced
1 large zucchini, sliced
1 small yellow squash, sliced
1 red bell pepper, seeded and cubed
6 roma tomatoes, halved
salt to taste
2 (5 oz) skinless boneless chicken breasts
3 tbsp olive oil

---

1. Preheat the oven to 400 degrees.
2. Spread the potatoes, zucchini, squash, pepper, and tomatoes in a glass baking dish.
3. Season this dish with the salt and pepper.
4. Meanwhile, score the flesh of each chicken breast 3-4 times using a sharp knife.
5. Lay the chicken on top of the vegetables.
6. Drizzle the olive oil over chicken.
7. Cover the dish with foil.
8. Bake for 30 minutes.
9. Remove the foil from the dish.
10. Return the dish to the oven.
11. Bake for 10 more minutes, or until the vegetables are juicy and the chicken is cooked through.

Hint: The juices from the chicken should run clear when pierced with a knife or toothpick.

Per serving: Calories: 318 Protein: 4g Carbs: 18g Fiber: 5gSugar: 5g Fat: 28g

Ginger Lime Chicken & Pumpkin

SERVES 2 / PREP TIME: 10 MINUTES / COOK TIME: 30 MINUTES

This refreshing pumpkin and lime dish makes a great autumn dinner!

---

1 lime, zested and juiced
1 tbsp pure maple syrup
1 tsp grated fresh ginger
2 (5 oz) skinless, boneless chicken breasts
1 tbsp olive oil
1 tbsp fresh ginger, sliced into thin strips

2 cups fresh pumpkin puree
salt and pepper to taste

---

1. Mix half the lime zest and all the lime juice with the maple syrup and grated ginger.
2. Score each chicken breast 3-4 times with a sharp knife.
3. Coat the breasts well with the marinade in a glass dish.
4. Set aside for 10 minutes so the chicken can marinate.
5. Meanwhile, preheat the broiler on low.
6. Line a baking tray with aluminum foil.
7. After it has marinated for 10 minutes, place the chicken breasts on the foil-lined tray.
8. Bake for 10-15 minutes under the broiler, flipping halfway through.
9. Bake until the chicken is cooked through and slightly caramelized.
10. While the chicken is baking, heat the oil in a small frying pan.
11. When the oil is hot, add the ginger strips.
12. Fry them for 1 minute, or until the ginger is crisp.
13. Strain out the ginger with a slotted spoon, leaving the oil in the pan.
14. Now stir the pumpkin puree into the ginger-infused oil.
15. Season the puree with the salt and pepper.
16. Sautee the puree until warmed through.
17. To serve, divide the pumpkin between 2 plates.
18. Top each plate with a chicken breast and the crisp ginger.

Hint: Green beans make a nice addition to this meal.

Per serving: Calories: 308 Protein: 33g Carbs: 21g Fiber: 3g Sugar: 10g Fat: 11g

Mexican Chicken and Pepper Tacos

SERVES 4 / PREP TIME: 5 MINUTES / COOK TIME: 45 MINUTES

This healthy taco recipe is sure to satisfy any taco craving!

---

1 (15 oz) can diced tomatoes
1 tbsp garlic infused olive oil
1 large handful fresh cilantro leaves, chopped
1 tbsp olive oil
1 red bell pepper, deseeded and thinly sliced
1 yellow bell pepper, deseeded and thinly sliced

4 (5 oz) skinless chicken breasts, cut into thin strips
1 pinch paprika
1 pinch ground cumin
1 pinch dried oregano
1 pinch dried cilantro
4 corn tortillas or gluten free wraps
½ iceberg lettuce head, finely shredded

---

1. Preheat the oven to 350 degrees.
2. For the salsa, combine the tomatoes, garlic infused oil, and cilantro in a bowl.
3. Cover this bowl and chill it for 30 minutes.
4. For the chicken, heat the oil in a wok or large nonstick frying pan.
5. Add the peppers.
6. Stir fry the peppers for 3-4 minutes.
7. Add the chicken, paprika, cumin, oregano, and cilantro.
8. Cook this for 10 minutes, or until the chicken is cooked through.
9. Meanwhile, wrap the tortillas in foil.
10. Warm them in the oven for 5 minutes.
11. Spoon one-quarter of the chicken mixture into the center of each tortilla.
12. Add a couple of tablespoons of salsa and some shredded lettuce to each tortilla.
13. Roll up and serve warm.

Per serving: Calories: 328 Protein: 35g Carbs: 22g Fiber: 6g Sugar: 6g Fat: 12g

Roasted Moroccan Spiced Chicken

SERVES 8 / PREP TIME: 20 MINUTES / COOK TIME: 40 MINUTES

This spiced chicken recipe is perfect for a dinner party!

---

2 lemons
2 tsp ground turmeric
2 tsp ground cumin
2 tbsp olive oil
salt and pepper to taste
8 (5 oz) skinless chicken breasts
4 cups red potatoes
1/2 tsp turmeric

---

1. Preheat the oven to 425 degrees.
2. Finely grate the zest from 1 lemon.
3. Squeeze the juice from both the lemons into a large, shallow dish.
4. Toss on the turmeric, cumin, half the oil, and some salt.
5. Place the chicken in this dish.
6. Cover the dish and set it aside to marinate.
7. Let marinade rest as long as possible.
8. Meanwhile, cut the potatoes in half.
9. Spread them over the bottom of a roasting dish.
10. Toss the potatoes in the remaining oil.
11. Sprinkle the potatoes with the turmeric and some salt.
12. Set the chicken on a rack above the potatoes in the oven.
13. Bake both dishes at the same time for 30-40 mins, or until the chicken is well browned and the potatoes are tender.

Per serving: Calories: 227 Protein: 32g Carbs: 8g Fiber: 1g Sugar: 1g Fat: 7g

North African Baked Chicken

SERVES 4 / PREP TIME: 10 MINUTES / COOK TIME: 50 MINUTES

The delicious spices of Northern Africa shine in this simple baked dish.

2 white potatoes, peeled and cut into 1 inch cubes	2 tbsp garlic infused olive oil
2 carrots, peeled and cut into 1 inch cubes	salt to taste
2 tbsp olive oil	4 (5 oz) chicken breasts
	1 lemon, quartered
	1 tsp ground cumin
	1 tsp turmeric

1. Preheat the oven to 400 degrees.
2. Place the potatoes and carrots into a roasting dish.
3. Drizzle the oil over the vegetables.
4. Season them well with the salt.
5. Place the dish in the oven to roast for 10 minutes.
6. Remove the dish from the oven.
7. Add the garlic infused oil and toss well.
8. Roast the dish for another 20 minutes.
9. Once roasted, remove the dish from the oven.
10. Add the chicken breasts and lemon quarters in a single layer over the vegetables.
11. Sprinkle everything with the spices.
12. Roast the chicken for 15-20 more minutes, or until the chicken is cooked through.
13. To serve, divide the chicken among four plates, each with a slice of roasted lemon for squeezing over the food.

Per serving: Calories: 389 Protein: 34g Carbs: 25g Fiber: 4g Sugar: 3g Fat: 17g

Homemade Tomato & Turkey Gnocchi

SERVES 4 / PREP TIME: 30 MINUTES / COOK TIME: 10 MINUTES

This delicious homemade gnocchi recipe is perfect for a cold winter evening!

---

4 large white potatoes, washed and peeled
1/2 cup brown rice flour
1 cup white rice flour
1/4 cup sorghum flour
1/4 cup tapioca flour
1 cup potato starch

2 egg whites, lightly beaten
salt to taste
water for boiling the gnocchi
1 tbsp garlic infused oil
1 cup tomatoes, diced
1 tbsp dried oregano
4 (5 oz) turkey breasts, cooked and

---

1. Slice the potatoes.
2. Steam them over high heat for about 10 minutes, or until tender.
3. Place the potatoes in a food processor and process until smooth.
4. Meanwhile, mix all the flours and the potato starch together by sifting through a mesh strainer into a mixing bowl.
5. Scrape the blended potato into this bowl,
6. Now add the lightly beaten egg whites.
7. Season this mixture with the salt.
8. Stir this mixture together until it forms a dough.
9. Turn out the dough onto a lightly floured surface.
10. Form it into a ball.
11. Cut the dough ball into four sections.
12. Roll out each section into a long cylinder about 4 inches wide.
13. Cut each cylinder into 1 1/4 inch pieces.
14. Meanwhile, boil a pot of water.
15. Add half the gnocchi to the water for approximately 3 minutes.
16. When the gnocchi float to the top of the water, they are done.
17. Scoop them off with a slotted spoon.
18. Place the gnocchi on serving plates.
19. Now heat the oil in a skillet over medium heat.
20. Add the diced tomatoes and herbs to the hot oil.
21. Add in the cooked turkey.
22. Allow this mixture to warm thoroughly, about 3 minutes.
23. Pour the tomatoes and turkey over the gnocchi as a light sauce.

Per serving: Calories: 750 Protein: 54g Carbs: 121g Sugar: 3g Fat: 7g

Crock Pot Turkey Stuffed Peppers

SERVES 4 / PREP TIME: 10 MINUTES / COOK TIME: 3-4 HOURS

These savory stuffed peppers cook while you're at work!

---

4 large bell peppers, a mix of colors
1 lb ground turkey
1 tbsp chopped fresh rosemary
1 tbsp chopped fresh oregano
1 medium stalk celery, chopped
1 tbsp garlic infused oil
2 cups cooked brown rice
3 cups diced tomatoes
1 cup feta cheese, crumbled
salt to taste
1 tbsp chives (green part only), thinly
sliced

---

1. Cut the tops off the bell peppers and remove the seeds.
2. In a medium bowl, mix the ground turkey, rosemary, oregano, celery, garlic oil, rice, 1 cup of the diced tomatoes, half the feta cheese, and the saltr to taste.
3. Spoon equal amounts of the meat mixture into the bell peppers.
4. Place the rest of the diced tomatoes into the bottom of the crock pot.
5. Add the peppers to the crock pot on top of the tomatoes.
6. Keeping the peppers sitting upright.
7. Turn the crock pot on high for 3-4 hours, or until the meat is cooked through.
8. 5 minutes before serving, sprinkle the remaining cheese on top of the cooked bell peppers.
9. Then top with the sliced chives.
10. To serve, drizzle the tomato sauce from the bottom of the crock pot on top of each pepper.

Per serving: Calories: 419 Protein: 35g Carbs: 37g Fiber: 6g Sugar: 8g Fat: 1g

Pan Fried Cilantro Cajun Chicken

SERVES 4 / PREP TIME: 20 MINUTES / COOK TIME: 20 MINUTES

This delicious concoction pairs well with a side salad.

¼ cup fresh cilantro, chopped roughly
2 green onions, green part only, chopped
3 tomatoes, diced
1 lime
1 tbsp olive oil
salt and pepper to taste

1 tsp dried oregano
2 tsp ground cumin
2 tsp ground cilantro seeds
2 tsp smoked paprika
½ tsp salt
4 (5 oz) skinless chicken breasts
1 tbsp olive oil

---

1. For the salsa, place the first 4 ingredients in a bowl.
2. Next, squeeze the lime over the salsa.
3. Toss in the oil with a little salt to taste.
4. Meanwhile, mix the oregano, and spices together in a shallow bowl.
5. Coat the chicken in this mixture.
6. Cover the chicken with parchment paper.
7. Beat the chicken with a rolling pin or meat mallet to flatten it out.
8. Now place the chicken in a pan with the oil over medium heat.
9. Cook the chicken for 15-20 minutes, turning half way through, until it is golden and cooked through.
10. Slice up the chicken and serve.

Per serving: Calories: 267 Protein: 33g Carbs: 9g Fiber: 3g Sugar: 4g Fat: 11g

Oriental Sweet & Sour Chicken

SERVES 3 / PREP TIME: 5 MINUTES / COOK TIME: 25 MINUTES

Delicious!

---

9 tbsp tomato paste
1 (20 oz) can pineapple chunks, drained
2 red bell peppers, seeded and cut into chunks
3 tbsp rice wine vinegar
4 tbsp stevia/coconut sugar
1 tbsp coconut oil
4 (5 oz) skinless and boneless chicken breast, sliced

1 cup cooked brown rice
1 green onions, sliced (green tips only)

---

1. In a large bowl, combine the tomato paste, pineapple, bell peppers, vinegar, and stevia/sugar.
2. Next, heat the oil in a skillet over medium-high heat.
3. Sauté the chicken breasts for 6-7 minutes before turning.
4. Sauté for 2-3 more minutes after turning them over.
5. Now add the sauce you mixed earlier.
6. Cover the skillet and let it simmer for 15 minutes, or until the chicken is thoroughly cooked.
7. Serve with cooked rice and a sprinkle of green onions.

Per serving: Calories: 502 Protein: 46g Carbs: 56g Fiber: 7g Sugar: 35g Fat: 1g

Chilled Thai Chicken Salad

SERVES 2 / PREP TIME: 30 MINUTES / COOK TIME: NA

This scrumptious hot-weather salad requires a marinade, like a chicken version of ceviche.

---

3 limes, juiced
1 tbsp fish sauce
1 tbsp coconut sugar
2 (4 oz) cooked skinless chicken
breasts, shredded
½ cucumber, cut into strips
1 tbsp chopped chives
1 tbsp fresh mint leaves

1 tbsp fresh cilantro leaves
½ cup beansprouts, cooked

---

1. To make the marinade, mix the lime juice, fish sauce, and sugar together until the sugar dissolves.
2. Add the rest of the ingredients to a salad bowl.
3. Drizzle the salad with the marinade.
4. Cover this bowl and store in the refrigerator until it is chilled all the way through, or at least 30 minutes.
5. Serve chilled.

Per serving: Calories: 188 Protein: 28g Carbs: 12g Fiber: 2g Sugar: 5g Fat: 4g

Chicken Tagine

SERVES 2 / PREP TIME: 5 MINUTES / COOK TIME: 3.5-4 HOURS SLOW COOKER

A Northern African inspired dish.

---

2 carrots, peeled and sliced
8oz of chicken breast, skinless and boneless, diced
1 cup of low fodmap chicken stock
1 cup water
2 tbsp of rice flour
2 tbsp of lemon juice, freshly squeezed
1 ½ tsp of ground cumin

1 ½ tsp of ground ginger
1 tsp of ground nutmeg
¾ tsp of ground black pepper
3 cups of cooked white rice
3 tbsp. of fresh cilantro, finely chopped

---

1. Add the carrots and chicken into the slow cooker.
2. In a bowl, whisk the broth, flour, lemon juice, cumin, ginger, nutmeg and the ground black pepper.
3. Add the mixture to the cooker along with the water.
4. Cover and cook on Low for 6 ½ to 7 hours or on High for 3 ½ to 4 hours.
5. Serve the rice in bowls with the turkey and the sauce on top.
6. Garnish with cilantro to finish.

Per serving: Calories: 215 Protein: 35g Carbs: 7g Fiber: 1g Sugar: 1g Fat: 5g

Chicken & Lemon Rice Stew

SERVES 3 / PREP TIME: 15 MINUTES / COOK TIME: 6-7 HOURS SLOW COOKER

Chicken and lemon pairs fantastically in this simple dish.

---

1 tbsp. of olive oil
8oz of chicken breasts, skinless and boneless, diced
½ cup chopped celery
1/3 cup of chopped carrot
1 cup of low fodmap chicken stock
1 cup of water
1 tsp. of dried oregano

A pinch of black pepper
1 cup of white rice, rinsed and drained
1 lemon, juiced
1/2 cucumber, washed and sliced
1 cup of spinach, washed
1 tbsp of extra virgin olive oil

---

1. Heat the oil in a skillet over a medium heat.
2. Add the chicken breast.
3. Cook for 3-5 minutes, stirring often until browned.
4. Stir in the celery and carrot.
5. Cook for 2 minutes, stirring occasionally.
6. Drain off the excess juices.
7. Into the slow cooker, add the chicken mixture and remaining ingredients (except lemon, extra virgin olive oil, cucumber and spinach).
8. Cover with the lid and cook on High for 30 minutes.
9. Reduce the heat to a Low.
10. Cook for 6-7 hours, or until the rice is tender and the liquid is absorbed.
11. Stir in the juice of half a lemon.
12. Slice the cucumber and mix with the spinach for the side salad.
13. Whisk the remaining lemon juice and olive oil together.
14. Dress the salad with the lemon and oil dressing.
15. Serve on the side of your chicken.

Per serving: Calories: 450 Protein: 29g Carbs: 54g Fiber: 2g Sugar: 0g Fat: 13g

Slow-Cooked Chicken Masala

SERVES 3 / PREP TIME: 15 MINUTES / COOK TIME: 3 HOURS SLOW COOKER

The fragrant spices release in the slow cooker, giving this dish an authentic taste.

8oz skinless, boneless chicken breast
1/2 red bell pepper, chopped
1/2 yellow bell pepper, chopped
1/2 cup green onions (green tips only), sliced
1 cup of low-fodmap chicken stock
1 tbsp of mild curry powder
1/4 tsp of turmeric

1/2 cup almond milk
1 tsp of cornstarch
1 cup white rice, cooked
2 tbsp of fresh cilantro, chopped

1. Combine the chicken, peppers, onions, stock, curry powder and turmeric in the slow cooker.
2. Cover and cook on Low for 8- 9 hours or on High for about 4½ hours.
3. In a small bowl, mix the almond milk and cornstarch until smooth.
4. Stir into chicken mixture.
5. If you're cooking on Low, turn up the heat to High now.
6. Cover and cook for 15 to 20 minutes more.
7. The sauce should be slightly thick by now.
8. Serve on white rice and sprinkle the with cilantro to finish.

Per serving: Calories: 259 Protein: 27g Carbs: 26g Fiber: 2g Sugar: 5g Fat: 5g

Fennel and Ginger Chicken

SERVES 4 / PREP TIME: 5 MINUTES / COOK TIME: 2.5-3 HOURS SLOW COOKER

The bold flavors of fennel, ginger and garlic are delicious, and sure to impress.

12oz of skinless boneless chicken breast, diced
1/4 tsp ground black pepper
1 bulb fennel, cored and cut into thin wedges
1 red bell pepper, de-seeded and diced
1 tsp fresh or dried rosemary
1 tsp of fresh or dried ginger (finely sliced if fresh)
½ cup low fodmap chicken stock
1 cup of water
1 tbsp of dried oregano

1. Sprinkle the chicken pieces with ground pepper.
2. Place the chicken into the slow cooker.
3. Top with fennel, bell pepper, rosemary and ginger.
4. Add the broth and water.
5. Cover and cook on Low for 5 to 6 hours or on High for 2½ to 3 hours.
6. Sprinkle each serving with oregano to finish.

Per serving: Calories: 166 Protein: 27g Carbs: 6g Fiber: 2g Sugar: 3g Fat: 4g

Rich Tomato & Red Pepper Chicken

SERVES 4 / PREP TIME: 5 MINUTES / COOK TIME: 3.5-4 HOURS SLOW COOKER

A tasty comforting slow cooked stew.

12oz skinless, boneless chicken thighs, cut into cubes
½ tsp of dried oregano
¼ tsp of ground black pepper
1 cup of low fodmap chicken stock
1 cup of water
1 medium red bell pepper, roughly chopped

1 cup sliced large tomatoes
1 tsp of cumin
1 cup of cooked white rice

1. In the slow cooker, combine the chicken, oregano and black pepper.
2. Add in the stock and water.
3. Cover and cook on Low for 7 to 8 hours or on High for 3 ½ to 4 hours.
4. If using Low, turn the heat up to High after 3.5-4 hours.
5. Stir in the red pepper, tomatoes and cumin.
6. Cover and cook for another 30 minutes.
7. Serve steaming hot with fluffy white rice.

Per serving: Calories: 179 Protein: 15g Carbs: 21g Fiber: 1g Sugar: 5g Fat: 4g

Caribbean Style Chicken Thighs

SERVES 2 / PREP TIME: 5 MINUTES / COOK TIME: 7-8 HOURS SLOW COOKER

Fragrant spiced chicken thighs with a lime and cilantro dressing.

1 tsp of cumin
1 tsp of cinnamon
1 tsp of dried oregano
1 tbsp garlic infused olive oil
8oz of chicken thighs, skinless and boneless
A pinch of black pepper
1 lime, juiced

2 tbsp of fresh cilantro, chopped

1. Mix the dry spices, herbs and garlic oil in a bowl to form your marinade.
2. Marinate the chicken thighs in the spice mix for as long as you've got!
3. Place in the bottom of the slow cooker in a single layer.
4. Cook for 7-8 hours on a low setting.
5. Meanwhile, prepare your salsa.
6. Remove the turkey thighs from the slow cooker.
7. Place them onto a chopping board.
8. Cut the thighs into slices.
9. Mix the lime juice and cilantro and drizzle over to serve.
10. Serve on a bed of salad.

Per serving: Calories: 272 Protein: 28g Carbs: 5g Fiber: 2g Sugar: 1g Fat: 16g

VEGETARIAN

Slow Cooked Autumn Root Vegetables

SERVES 6 / PREP TIME: 10 MINUTES / COOK TIME: 3-4 HOURS SLOW COOKER

Satisfying root vegetables slow cooked to perfection.

1 cup of boiling water
1 tbsp of rice flour
1 small rutabaga, peeled and cubed
2 large carrots, peeled and cubed
2 turnips, peeled and cubed
1 cup of low fodmap vegetable stock
2 tbsp of dried oregano
freshly ground black pepper, to taste

1. Dissolve the flour in the boiling water and transfer to the slow cooker pot.
2. Add all of the remaining ingredients to the slow cooker.
3. Set the slow cooker to LOW for 3-4 hours until cooked through.

Per serving: Calories: 35 Protein: 2g Carbs: 7g Fiber: 2g Sugar: 3g Fat: 0g

Greek Rice

Rice can be a pain to cook, but not with this recipe. The Greek flavors add an extra touch.

1 tbsp of garlic-infused olive oil
2 cups of white rice
3 cups of water
1 cup of lo fodmap vegetable stock
1 red bell pepper, seeds and pith removed, and finely chopped
1 green bell pepper, seeds and pith removed, and finely chopped

1 cup of crumbled feta cheese
2 tbsp of lemon juice

1. Heat a tablespoon of olive oil in a deep frying pan over medium heat.
2. Add the rice and sauté until the rice is nicely browned and transfer to the slow cooker pot.
3. Add the water and stock to the pan, and de-glaze the frying pan. Transfer to the slow cooker.
4. Set the slow cooker to HIGH.
5. With 30 minutes left of the cooking time, fluff the rice, and mix in the bell peppers, and cheese.
6. When the rice is cooked to your desired consistency, stir in the lemon juice.

Per serving: Calories: 332 Protein: 9g Carbs: 54g Fiber: 1g Sugar: 3g Fat: 8g

Roasted Eggplant

SERVES 2 / PREP TIME: 10 MINUTES / COOK TIME: 40 MINUTES

Delicious Middle Eastern Flavors.

---

4 cups eggplant (approx. 1 medium eggplant, diced)
A pinch of salt
2 tbsp garlic-infused olive oil
1 tbsp fresh basil leaves, torn
1 tbsp dried oregano
1 lemon, juiced

---

1. Preheat the oven to 300f/150/gas mark 2.
2. Slice the eggplant in half lengthways.
3. Use the knife to lightly score across the flesh in crosses.
4. Sprinkle with salt and leave for a few minutes.
5. Line an oven tray with parchment paper.
6. Place the eggplant on the tray (skin side down).
7. Drizzle over the oil and parsley.
8. Roast in the oven for 30-40 minutes or until very soft.
9. Serve with the fresh basil and a squeeze of lemon juice.

Per serving: Calories: 191 Protein: 2g Carbs: 18g Fiber: 5g Sugar: 6g Fat: 14g

Mixed Vegetable Minestrone Soup

SERVES 5 / PREP TIME: 5 MINUTES / COOK TIME: 35 MINUTES

A classic!

---

2 tbsp olive oil
1 celery stalk, sliced
2 medium carrots, peeled and diced
2 medium potatoes, peeled and diced
2 medium zucchinis, peeled and diced
2 cups low FODMAP vegetable stock
1 cup beef tomatoes, diced
½ tsp dried parsley

½ tsp dried basil
A pinch of salt and pepper
1 1/2 cups gluten free macaroni pasta

---

1. In a large soup pot, sauté the celery and carrot in olive oil until soft.
2. Add the potato, zucchini, tomatoes, vegetable broth, herbs, salt, and pepper.
3. Bring to a rolling boil.
4. Lower the heat slightly and allow to simmer for 20 minutes.
5. Add the gluten free pasta to the pot.
6. Simmer for 15 minutes until all the pasta is thoroughly cooked.

Per serving: Calories: 274 Protein: 8g Carbs: 46g Fiber: 5g Sugar: 0g Fat: 7g

Gluten Free Tomato & Basil Pasta

SERVES 2 / PREP TIME: 5 MINUTES / COOK TIME: 15 MINUTES

Ready in a flash!

---

1 ½ cup gluten free penne pasta (or
equivalent shape)
½ cup beef tomatoes, finely diced and
juices reserved
1 tbsp garlic-infused olive oil
1 lemon, juiced
A pinch of salt and pepper
1 tbsp fresh basil, torn

---

1. Cook pasta according to package directions.
2. Drain and allow to cool.
3. Mix through the tomatoes, oil, lemon juice and salt and pepper.
4. Top with torn basil and serve!

Per serving: Calories: 426 Protein: 14g Carbs: 73g Fiber: 6g Sugar: 4g Fat: 9g

Herby Carrot and Lemon Soup

SERVES 4 / PREP TIME:15 MINUTES / COOK TIME: 7-8 HOURS SLOW COOKER

This soup is amazing and fresh.

1 tbsp of olive oil
1 tsp of fennel seeds, crushed
1 tbsp of ground ginger
4 medium carrots, peeled and chopped
1 cup green onions (green tips only),
diced
1 lemon, zest and juice

4 cups of water
2 tbsp of fresh oregano, chopped
freshly ground black pepper, to taste

1. Heat the oil in a skillet over a medium heat.
2. Add the crushed mustard seeds and fennel seeds and stir-fry for a minute.
3. Add the ground ginger and cook for another minute.
4. Add the carrots, onions, and lemon juice and cook until the vegetables are softened, about 5 minutes.
5. Remove from the heat and transfer to the slow cooker pot.
6. Add the water, lemon zest, and fresh oregano to the pot.
7. Season generously with freshly ground black pepper.
8. Set the slow cooker to LOW for 7-8 hours overnight.

Per serving: Calories: 66 Protein: 1g Carbs: 9g Fiber: 3g Sugar: 3g Fat: 4g

Veggie Quinoa & Parsley Burgers

SERVES 4 / PREP TIME: 10 MINUTES / COOK TIME: 15 MINUTES

Packed with protein and succulent flavors – you won't miss the meat!

1 tbsp. olive oil
1 tsp ground cumin
1 medium zucchini, diced
3/4 cup quinoa, cooked
1 medium carrot, peeled and grated
1 stalk celery, sliced
1 tbsp dried parsley
A pinch of salt and pepper
2 egg whites

1 tbsp quinoa flour
1 cup organic spinach, washed

1. Add the first 8 ingredients for the burgers into a mixing bowl and stir well.
2. Then, add your egg and quinoa flour and stir.
3. Form between 4 veggie patties and dust with a little extra quinoa powder.
4. Place the veggie patties on a covered plate or in a container and set aside in the refrigerator to cool for at least either an hour or overnight.
5. In a skillet, heat the olive oil and cook the patties for 6-7 minutes on each side or until golden brown on the outside and piping hot in the middle.
6. Serve with your choice of salad.

Per serving: Calories: 191 Protein: 8g Carbs: 28g Fiber: 5g Sugar: 3g Fat: 6g

Roasted Tomato & Basil Soup

SERVES 5 / PREP TIME: 10 MINUTES / COOK TIME: 50 MINUTES

The roasted tomatoes add a real sweet kick to a traditional tomato soup.

5 beef tomatoes, halved
1 tbsp. olive oil
A pinch salt and pepper
2 cups low FODMAP vegetable stock
1 cup water
1/2 cup + 1 tbsp. fresh basil, torn

1. Preheat the oven to 300f/150/gas mark 2.
2. Add the tomatoes to a lined oven tray.
3. Then, drizzle the oil over the tomatoes and sprinkle salt and pepper.
4. Roast the tomatoes for 20-30 minutes until lightly browned.
5. Into a large saucepan or a stockpot over a medium heat, add the roasted tomatoes, 1/2 cup basil, broth and water.
6. Bring to a gentle boil and then lower the heat and allow to simmer for 20 minutes.
7. Remove the tomato mixture from the heat and then let it cool off for around an hour.
8. Remove and allow to cool slightly before blending with a stick blender or in a processor.
9. Scatter the torn basil over the top and serve.

Per Serving: Calories: 34 Protein: 2 g Carbs: 7g Fiber: 2g Sugar: 4g Fat: 0g

Spinach, Carrot, and Quinoa Salad

SERVES 4 / PREP TIME: 5 MINUTES / COOK TIME: 15 MINUTES

A refreshing vegan salad.

---

1 cup quinoa
1 tbsp. olive oil
½ tsp. cumin
½ tsp. paprika
1 1/3 cups water
2 cups organic spinach, washed
1 carrot, peeled and grated
2 beef tomatoes, washed and sliced
1 tbsp. fresh chives, chopped
1 lime, juiced
A pinch of salt and pepper

---

1. First, rinse the quinoa in cold water.
2. Drain the quinoa and set aside.
3. Use a medium saucepan to heat up the oil over a medium heat.
4. Then, add the spices, stirring for 30 seconds.
5. Add the quinoa to the pan and stir.
6. Continue cooking for 2 minutes whilst stirring.
7. Now add the water and turn down to a simmer for 10 minutes the water has mostly been absorbed.
8. Spread the quinoa over the bottom of a shallow bowl and allow it to cool down to room temperature.
9. Mix the cooked quinoa with the carrots, tomatoes, spinach and chives.
10. Combine the oil and lime juice into the salad and scatter over the lime zest.
11. Season with salt and pepper to serve.

Per Serving: Calories: 205 Protein: 7g Carbs: 32g Fiber: 5g Sugar: 3g Fat: 6g

Mason Jar Pineapple & Rice Salad

SERVES 2 / PREP TIME: 5 MINUTES / COOK TIME: 20 MINUTES

Deliciously sweet!

---

1 cup red jasmine rice
1 cup canned pineapple, peeled and
cubed
1 tbsp freshly chopped mint
1 tsp olive oil
1 tsp white wine vinegar
A pinch of salt and pepper
2 cups organic spinach, washed
2 glass mason jars

---

1. Cook the rice according to package directions.
2. Whisk the oil, vinegar and salt and pepper together to form your dressing.
3. Into a mason jar, layer the rice followed with spinach, then mango cubes. Press down and repeat until the jar is almost full.
4. When ready to eat, pour over a little dressing, place the lid on securely, give it a little shake and enjoy!

Per Serving: Calories: 176, Protein: 4g , Carbs: 35g , Fiber: 3g, Sugar: 10g, Fat: 3g

Potato & Scallion Soup

SERVES 5 / PREP TIME: 10 MINUTES / COOK TIME: 30 MINUTES

Wholesome and fresh.

---

2 cups low FODMAP vegetable stock
1 cup rice milk
5 small white potatoes, peeled and diced
2 tbsp chives, chopped
2 carrots, peeled and diced

¼ cup scallions (green tips only), sliced
1 tbsp olive oil
1 tbsp dried parsley
1 tsp dried rosemary
A pinch of sea salt

---

1. Into a large stock pot, add the vegetable stock, milk, potatoes, chives, carrots and scallions and bring to a boil over a high heat.
2. Next, add in the olive oil, parsley, rosemary, and salt.
3. Lower the heat and allow the mixture to simmer for 30 minutes until the potatoes are tender, whilst occasionally stirring to prevent the bottom from sticking – if it starts to dry out simply add a little water/milk.
4. Be sure to occasionally stir the mixture.
5. Allow to cool slightly and blend until smooth.
6. Serve hot!

Per Serving: Calories: 102, Protein: 2g, Carbs: 16g, Fiber: 2g, Sugar: 5g, Fat: 3g

Pumpkin and Tomato Vegetable Soup

SERVES 4 / PREP TIME: 5 MINUTES / COOK TIME: 1 HOUR AND 15 MINUTES

This savory soup makes the perfect dinner treat!

---

2 tbsp olive oil
1 tbsp garlic infused olive oil
3 tomatoes, coarsely chopped
1 cup water
1 bundle of herbs tied with a string: 1 bay leaf, 2 thyme sprigs, and 1 rosemary sprig
1 pinch salt
2 medium carrots, julienned

1 turnip, diced
1 (15 oz) cup pumpkin puree
1 cup water
1 cup fresh or frozen spinach
1 cup quinoa
1 tsp dried oregano

---

1. Heat the olive oil in a large, deep pan over medium-high heat.
2. Reduce the heat to medium.
3. Add the tomatoes and let them cook for 15 minutes, or until they turn into a thick sauce.
4. Add the water and the bundle of herbs.
5. Bring the water to a boil.
6. Sprinkle the water with the salt.
7. Now add the carrots, turnip and pumpkin.
8. Reduce the heat to minimum.
9. Simmer for 40 minutes, or until the vegetables are tender yet crisp.
10. Next add more water, the spinach, and the quinoa and cook over medium-low heat for 20 minutes.
11. Remove the bundle.
12. Sprinkle the oregano over the soup.
13. Ladle it into bowls to serve.

Per serving: Calories: 319 Protein: 8g Carbs: 45g Fiber: 9g Sugar: 10g Fat: 13g

Carrot and Cucumber Spring Rolls

SERVES 2 / PREP TIME: 20 MINUTES / COOK TIME: 10 MINUTES

This nearly no-cook method will give you restaurant-quality spring rolls in no time!

---

2 medium carrots, peeled
1/2 cucumber
1 medium zucchini, peeled and sliced
1 tbsp fresh cilantro, chopped
1 tsp low sodium soy sauce
1 tsp rice wine vinegar
1/2 tsp sesame oil
water to boil the noodles
1 oz rice noodles (about 1/3 of 8 oz

container)
10 spring roll wrappers
1/2 tsp sesame oil
1 tsp rice wine vinegar
1 tsp fresh cilantro, chopped

---

1. Julienne the carrots, cucumber, and zucchini, keeping each vegetable separate.
2. Make the dressing for the carrots by mixing the cilantro, soy sauce, rice wine vinegar, and sesame oil.
3. Drizzle this over the julienned carrots in small bowl.
4. Meanwhile, in large saucepan, boil the water in preparation for the rice noodles.
5. Cook them according to package directions.
6. Drain the noodles and set them aside.
7. Hydrate the spring roll wrappers by adding then individually to a large bowl filled with very warm water.
8. Remove them from water when they are fully pliable.
9. Place them on a plastic cutting board.
10. Place the noodles and veggies near the edge of each wrapper.
11. Roll them up burrito-style.
12. Meanwhile, create a light dipping sauce with sesame oil, rice wine vinegar, and a sprinkling of the cilantro to taste.
13. Cut the spring rolls diagonally and enjoy.

Hint: When julienning the vegetables, slice primarily the outer skin, not the center.

Per serving: Calories: 277, Protein: 6g Carbs: 58g, Sugar: 5g, Fat: 3g

Quinoa and Carrot Salad with Lemon

SERVES 3 / PREP TIME: 15 MINUTES / COOK TIME: N/A

This filling salad can be an entire meal by itself!

1/4 cup garlic infused olive oil
1/2 tbsp fresh lemon juice
1 cup fresh cilantro leaves, washed
salt to taste
1 cup red quinoa, cooked as directed
2 small carrots, peeled and sliced
1 small zucchini, peeled and sliced
1/4 cup black olives, sliced

1/2 cup roma tomatoes, cut into wedges
2 cups fresh spinach, washed
3/4 cup canned chickpeas
1 yellow bell pepper, de-seeded and thinly sliced

1. In a blender, add the garlic infused oil, fresh lemon juice, cilantro leaves, salt, and blend to mix.
2. Set the dressing aside.
3. In a serving bowl, place the cooked quinoa.
4. Top the quinoa with the rest of the ingredients and the dressing.
5. Serve by scooping the salad into individual bowls.

Per serving: Calories: 368 Protein: 9g Carbs: 37g Fiber: 8g Sugar: 6g Fat: 22g

Zucchini and Carrot "Spaghetti"

SERVES 2 / PREP TIME: 5 MINUTES / COOK TIME: 15 MINUTES

This fun recipe transforms spaghetti into a gluten-free, low carb masterpiece.

---

2 medium zucchinis
1 tbsp garlic infused oil
2 large tomatoes, diced
2 medium carrots, peeled
1 small poblano pepper, de-seeded and

sliced
salt and pepper to taste
1 tbsp olive oil

---

1. Using a spiralizer or julienne, julienne the zucchini flesh and set it aside.
2. In a large skillet, add the garlic infused oil, tomatoes, carrots, and pepper.
3. Sauté them for about 3 minutes.
4. Add in the zucchini.
5. Stir and cook until the veggies are fork tender, about 10 minutes.
6. Season with the salt and pepper.
7. Drizzle the "spaghetti" with olive oil to serve.

Per serving: Calories: 206 Protein: 4g Carbs: 18g Fiber: 6g Sugar: 12g Fat: 15g

Spinach and Feta Fusilli

SERVES 2 / PREP TIME: 10 MINUTES / COOK TIME: 15 MINUTES

This fast gluten free pasta recipe might surprise you with how flavorful it is.

7 oz gluten free fusilli
1 tbsp garlic infused olive oil
2 cups fresh or frozen spinach, washed and drained
1 tsp crushed red pepper flakes
2 tbsp feta cheese, crumbled

salt to taste
2 tbsp fresh basil, torn

1. Cook the fusilli according to package instructions.
2. Drain it and set it aside.
3. Next, heat the oil in a skillet over medium-high heat.
4. Add the spinach.
5. Sauté it for 5 minutes, or until it has wilted.
6. Add in the cooked pasta, red pepper flakes, and feta cheese.
7. Quickly give everything a big stir.
8. Season it generously with the salt, and basil.
9. Toss well and serve.

Per serving: Calories: 224 Protein: 7g Carbs: 27g Sugar: 3g Fat: 12g

Red Quinoa and Pumpkin Stew

SERVES 2 / PREP TIME: 15 MINUTES / COOK TIME: 1 HOUR AND 15 MINUTES

This thick tomato stew will satisfy anyone's craving for a meat stew.

3 tbsp garlic infused olive oil	1 pinch salt
1 stalk celery, diced	2 medium carrots, julienned
3 large tomatoes, coarsely chopped	1 turnip, diced
1 cup water	1 cup fresh cooked pumpkin, diced
1 bundle of herbs tied with a string: 1 bay leaf, 2 fresh thyme sprigs, and 1 fresh rosemary sprig	1 cup water
	1 cup fresh spinach
	1 cup red quinoa

1. Heat the olive oil in a large deep pan over medium heat.
2. Add the celery and the tomatoes.
3. Let them cook for 15 minutes, or until it has turned into a thick sauce.
4. Add the water and the bundle of herbs.
5. Bring this to a boil.
6. Sprinkle in the salt and add the carrots, turnip, and pumpkin.
7. Reduce the heat to low.
8. Simmer the stew like this for 40 minutes, or until the vegetables are tender yet crisp.
9. Next, add the other cup of water, the spinach, and the red quinoa.
10. Cook this over medium-low heat for about 20 minutes.
11. Remove the bundle herbs before serving.

Per serving: Calories: 606 Protein: 16g Carbs: 81g Fiber: 15g Sugar: 16g Fat: 26g

Healthy Potatoes Dauphinoise

SERVES 4 / PREP TIME: 10 MINUTES / COOK TIME: 1 HOUR

This one-dish gourmet meal is sure to impress guests!

---

4 small white potatoes, sliced thinly
1 cup fresh cooked pumpkin, sliced thinly
1 tbsp coconut oil
2 tbsp corn or potato starch

1 cup canned coconut milk
1 ½ tsp salt
1 tbsp fresh thyme, leaves only

---

1. Preheat the oven to 350 degrees.
2. Start layering the thinly sliced potatoes and pumpkin in a 9x13 baking dish.
3. Set this aside.
4. Use a medium saucepan to heat the coconut oil over medium-low heat until it is melted.
5. Add the potato starch.
6. Stir until the potato starch is smooth.
7. Allow it to simmer until the mixture turns light golden, about 5 minutes.
8. Meanwhile, heat the milk in a small saucepan or in the microwave.
9. Gradually add the warm milk to the potato starch by whisking continuously until it is very smooth.
10. Bring this to a boil.
11. Cook for 10 minutes, stirring constantly.
12. Remove this from heat.
13. Season it with the salt.
14. Pour it over the potatoes and pumpkin.
15. Transfer the baking dish to the oven.
16. Bake it for 45 minutes to one hour.
17. Top the dish with fresh thyme to serve.

Hint: Use light coconut milk to reduce the amount of saturated fat.

Per serving: Calories: 361 Protein: 6g Carbs: 48g Fiber: 7g Sugar: 4g Fat: 18g

Zucchini Citrus Veggie Fritters

SERVES 4 /   PREP TIME: 10 MINUTES /   COOK TIME: 30 MINUTES

These large fritters can be used as veggie burgers to keep you on track!

½ cup quinoa grain
1 cup boiling water
1 pinch of salt
4 tbsp olive oil
2 cups zucchini, diced
1/2 cup millet
½ cup chopped fresh parsley
¼ cup chives (green tops only), chopped

½ lemon, zest only
2 tbsp lemon juice
½ cup canned chickpeas
½ tsp salt
½ tsp cumin
2 egg whites
2 tbsp rice flour
coconut oil for frying

---

1. Place the quinoa in a saucepan with the boiling water and the salt.
2. Lower the heat.
3. Cover the pot and simmer for 15 minutes, or until the quinoa is cooked.
4. When it's done, stir it with a fork to loosen the grains and set it aside.
5. In the meantime, heat a large non-stick pan over medium high heat with the olive oil.
6. Add the zucchini.
7. Cook until the zucchini is golden and tender, about 10 minutes.
8. In a large mixing bowl, combine the millet, parsley, chives, lemon zest, and lemon juice, and set it aside.
9. Add the chickpeas to a food processor and pulse until they are ground up.
10. Transfer them to the large mixing bowl with the herbed millet mixture.
11. Add in the zucchini, salt, cumin, egg whites, and flour.
12. Mix this together with your hands until it is well combined.
13. Divide the mixture into 4 big patties.
14. Lightly coat the bottom of the skillet with the coconut oil.
15. Add the veggie fritters and cook them until a golden crust forms, about 5 to 6 minutes.
16. Flip them to the other side and cook them another 5 minutes, or until that side is also golden.

Per serving: Calories: 429 Protein: 11g Carbs: 46g Fiber: 6g Sugar: 4g Fat: 23g

Grilled Citrus Fennel Hearts

SERVES 2 / PREP TIME: 5 MINUTES / COOK TIME: 20 MINUTES

These scrumptious hearts pair well with a salad.

---

2 small fennel hearts, sliced
2 tablespoons extra virgin olive oil
2 tablespoons fresh lemon juice
1/2 lemon, zest only
Salt to taste

---

1. Place the fennel hearts, oil, lemon juice, and zest in a shallow dish,
2. Season everything with salt.
3. Toss it to coat well.
4. Let the dish stand to marinate for at least 10 minutes.
5. To cook, toss the fennel slices on a barbecue grill or a nonstick pan for 5-10 minutes on each side, turning several times with tongs, until they are crisp-tender and the edges are slightly charred.
6. Drizzle the hearts with additional olive oil to serve.

Per serving: Calories: 196 Protein: 3g Carbs: 18g Sugar: 9g Fat: 15g

Tossed Brown Rice and Spinach Bowl

SERVES 2 / PREP TIME: 10 MINUTES / COOK TIME: 35 MINUTES

This filling and tasty rice bowl is sure to perk up your afternoon!

---

1 cup brown rice
2 cups boiling water
1 pinch salt
2 medium carrots, peeled and sliced

4 tbsp lemon juice
1 tbsp olive oil
2 cups fresh spinach
1 tbsp olive oil
1 tbsp apple cider vinegar
1 pinch of salt
1 handful pumpkin seeds

---

1. Place the rice in a pot with the boiling water and the pinch of salt.
2. Simmer on low heat until all the water has been absorbed and the rice is cooked, about 30 minutes.
3. In the meantime, steam the carrots for about thirty minutes in a saucepan over medium heat.
4. When they are done, place them in a bowl.
5. Mash the carrots with a fork.
6. Now mix in the lemon juice.
7. Next, it's time to heat the olive oil in a pan over medium-high heat.
8. Add the spinach and sauté for 5 minutes, or until the spinach has wilted.
9. Remove the spinach.
10. Mix the olive oil, vinegar, and salt together in a small bowl to make the dressing.
11. Place everything else in a serving bowl.
12. Pour the dressing over the bowl.
13. Finally, toss in the pumpkin seeds and serve.

Per serving: Calories: 523 Protein: 10 Carbs: 80 Fiber: 8 Sugar: 5 Fat: 19 (Unsaturated: 16 Saturated: 3)

Quinoa and Eggplant Boats

SERVES 4 / PREP TIME: 5 MINUTES / COOK TIME: 55 MINUTES

Stuffed and roasted eggplants.

water to boil eggplant
2 medium eggplants, halved lengthwise
2 tbsp olive oil
2 tsp kosher salt
2 cups fresh spinach, washed
5 oz crumbled goat cheese
1 cup quinoa, cooked

3 tbsp gluten-free breadcrumbs
1 lemon, zest only
1 tbsp chopped fresh parsley
salt to taste

1. Preheat the oven to 400 degrees.
2. Bring a large pan of water to a boil.
3. Add the eggplant halves and cook for 4-5 mins.
4. Drain the eggplant well.
5. Pat them dry with paper towels.
6. Place the eggplant on a baking sheet.
7. Brush the eggplant with half the olive oil.
8. Bake in the oven for 20-25 minutes, or until tender and golden.
9. Remove the eggplant from the oven.
10. Scoop out the flesh, leaving about 1/4 inch of flesh attached to the skin.
11. Set the skins aside.
12. Now roughly chop the eggplant flesh.
13. Meanwhile, heat the remaining oil in a large frying pan.
14. Add the eggplant flesh to the pan and fry for a few minutes.
15. Add the spinach and cook for 3-4 minutes, or until the spinach is wilted, stirring frequently.
16. Remove the pan from the heat.
17. Stir in the cheese and quinoa.
18. In a separate bowl, mix together the breadcrumbs, lemon zest, parsley, and salt.
19. Spoon the spinach mixture into the eggplant halves.
20. Sprinkle the top of each eggplant with the breadcrumb mixture.
21. Return this to the oven.
22. Bake for 10-15 minutes, or until the topping is golden.

Per serving: Calories: 325 Protein: 14g Carbs: 28g Fiber: 10g Sugar: 11g Fat: 19g

Carrot Infused Potato Gnocchi

SERVES 4 / PREP TIME: 20 MINUTES / COOK TIME: 30 MINUTES

This simple carrot and potato gnocchi is sure to delight everyone's taste buds!

---

1 oz fresh cilantro, torn
1 tbsp garlic infused oil
1 tbsp extra-virgin olive oil
7 oz potatoes
2 cups cooked carrots, mashed
2 egg whites
1 1/4 cup brown rice flour
2 tbsp crumbled feta cheese

---

1. For the sauce, add the cilantro to a food processor with the two oils.
2. Blend the cilantro mixture to a paste.
3. Set it aside for later.
4. Peel and boil the potatoes for 20 minutes, or until soft.
5. Add the cooked carrot and potato to a mixing bowl.
6. Mash the cooked potato and carrots with a masher or a large fork until the mixture is smooth.
7. Add the egg whites, coconut flour, and cheese to the bowl.
8. Mix everything together with your hands until you have a smooth dough.
9. Divide the dough into four balls.
10. On a lightly floured surface or table, roll each ball of potato dough into a long sausage roll.
11. Then, using a table knife, cut each roll into 1 inch pieces to form gnocchi.
12. Press each gnocchi with a fork to make a ridged pattern.
13. Bring a large pan of water to a boil with a pinch of salt.
14. Place 10 gnocchi at a time carefully into the water.
15. Boil them for about 30 seconds.
16. The gnocchi will rise to the surface of the water when they are cooked.
17. Remove the gnocchi from the water with a slotted spoon.
18. Place the cooked gnocchi into warm bowls.
19. Stir in a teaspoonful of the sauce to serve.

Hint: If the dough becomes sticky, you can simply add more flour.

Per serving: Calories: 314 Protein: 7g Carbs: 51g Fiber: 5g Sugar: 4g Fat: 9g

Vegetarian Feta & Tomato Quiche

SERVES 4 / PREP TIME: 1 HOUR / COOK TIME: 1 HOUR

This very traditional quiche recipe is well worth the extra effort!

---

3 oz rice flour
3 oz fine cornmeal
3 oz potato flour
1 tsp xanthan gum
1 pinch of salt
5 oz coconut oil, cold
1 egg white, lightly beaten

2 tbsp cold water
1 cup tomatoes, diced
1 tbsp olive oil
salt to taste
½ cup feta cheese
3 egg whites
1 tbsp basil leaves, torn

---

1. Sift the rice flour, fine cornmeal, potato flour, xanthan gum and salt into a bowl and mix well.
2. Cut the cold oil into cubes and gently work into the flour mixture with your hands.
3. Make a well in the center of the flour; add 1 egg white and water.
4. Mix the pastry dough together using a fork and roll into a ball with your hands.
5. On a lightly floured board, gently knead the dough with the heel of your hand for a few minutes to form a silky-smooth ball. Flatten the ball slightly before wrapping it in plastic wrap and refrigerating for about 30 minutes.
6. Roll out the pastry dough and lift up with rolling pin. Drape it over the pie pan so that the crust hangs over the sides a little.
7. Gently push the pastry into the corners of the pie pan. Chill the pie pan in the fridge or freezer for 20 minutes.
8. Meanwhile, preheat oven to 400 degrees.
9. Add the tomatoes with the olive oil, and salt to a baking dish in the oven.
10. Returning to the pie crust, take it out of the fridge or freezer and lightly prick the bottom of the crust all over with a fork.
11. Cover the dough with a circle of aluminum foil or parchment paper and fill it with ceramic baking beans - blind bake for 20 mins.
12. Remove the crust from the oven and take out the foil and beans before returning to oven for 5-10 mins, or until light brown. Remove crust and tomatoes from oven.
13. In the meantime, beat 3 egg whites in a large bowl and stir in most of the basil.
14. Sprinkle half the cheese over the bottom, then spread the tomatoes, egg whites, and the rest of the cheese over the top and bake for 20-25 minutes, or until set and golden brown - serve!

Per serving: Calories: 535 Protein: 11g Carbs: 54g Sugar: 3g Fat: 32g

Zesty Lime Eggplant

SERVES 4 / PREP TIME: 10 MINUTES / COOK TIME: 25 MINUTES

This sweet and zesty quinoa is filling and satisfying!

---

2 tbsp coconut oil
2 tbsp pure maple syrup
2 small eggplants, cut into wedges
1 red bell pepper, deseeded and diced
1 ½ cups red quinoa
boiling water to cook the quinoa
1 lime, zested and juiced
1 tbsp fresh mint leaves, chopped

---

1. Mix together the oil and maple syrup.
2. Next, drizzle half the syrup mixture over the eggplants and pepper.
3. Heat a nonstick frying pan over medium heat.
4. Cook the vegetables for 10-15 mins, turning them until they are lightly charred and cooked through.
5. Set aside the vegetables until you're ready to serve.
6. Meanwhile, pour the quinoa into a large bowl.
7. Pour boiling water over it so it is well covered.
8. Let it sit for 10 minutes until the quinoa is softened and plump.
9. Drain the quinoa.
10. Next, pour the remaining dressing, the lime juice, the lime zest, and the mint leaves over the quinoa.
11. Toss the quinoa bowl to mix it together.
12. Serve the roasted vegetables in bowls on top of the quinoa.

Per serving: Calories: 395 Protein: 11g Carbs: 66g Fiber: 14g Sugar: 20g Fat: 11g

Parsley and Quinoa Tabbouleh

SERVES 2 / PREP TIME: 5 MINUTES / COOK TIME: 20 MINUTES

This healthy tabbouleh recipe will add flavor to any Mediterranean dish!

---

1 cup quinoa
2 cups water
1 lemon, juiced and zested
2 tbsp olive oil
2 tbsp fresh mint, chopped
2 tbsp fresh flat-leaf parsley, chopped

1 tbsp green onions, chopped
½ cucumber, diced
salt to taste
1/4 cup shredded lettuce

---

1. Rinse the quinoa well.
2. Place it in a pan with 2 cups of water.
3. Bring the pan to a boil.
4. Cover the quinoa, reduce the heat, and gently simmer it for 20 minutes, or until most of the water has been soaked up.
5. Turn off the heat and leave the lid on so it can steam for a few minutes.
6. Drain any remaining water.
7. Into the quinoa, stir the lemon juice and the olive oil.
8. Allow it to cool fully.
9. Finally, stir in the other ingredients before serving.

Per serving: Calories: 440 Protein: 12g Carbs: 58g Fiber: 8g Sugar: 4g Fat: 19g

Mediterranean Grilled Vegetables

SERVES 5 / PREP TIME: 5 MINUTES / COOK TIME: 30 MINUTES

So simple yet so scrumptious!

---

2 large eggplants, cubed
2 red bell peppers, seeded and sliced
into 4 pieces
4 small zucchinis
4 large tomatoes

4 tbsp olive oil
1 tbsp red wine vinegar
1 tsp coconut sugar
1/8 cup fresh basil, torn
1 tbsp garlic infused oil
1 tbsp chopped chives (green tips only)
salt to taste

---

1. Preheat the broiler/grill to a medium low heat.
2. Spread the vegetables out across a lined oven tray.
3. In another bowl, stir together the rest of the ingredients.
4. Pour over the vegetables and toss to coat.
5. Broil/grill for 25-30 minutes until soft and lightly browned.
6. Remove and enjoy hot or allow to cool and refrigerate to serve as an aintipasti on a summer's day!

Per serving: Calories: 237 Protein: 5g Carbs: 25 Fiber: 10g Sugar: 17g Fat: 15g

Italian Eggplant Lasagna

SERVES 6 / PREP TIME: 10 MINUTES / COOK TIME: 1 HOUR

This delectable lasagna is so rich, you don't even miss the meat!

---

2 tbsp olive oil, plus extra for brushing
1 tbsp garlic infused oil
2 fresh thyme sprigs
8 large fresh sage leaves, finely chopped
4 cans diced tomatoes
3 tbsp red wine vinegar

3 tbsp coconut sugar
1 large eggplant, sliced lengthways as thinly as you can
1 cup crumbled goat cheese
1 tbsp dried oregano
1 tbsp dried basil
salt to taste

---

1. Preheat the oven to 400 degrees.
2. Heat the oil in a large skillet.
3. For the sauce, add the thyme and sage, cooking gently for a few minutes.
4. Add in the tomatoes, vinegar, and sugar.
5. Gently simmer the tomatoes for 20-25 minutes, or until thickened a little, removing from the heat when they are done.
6. Meanwhile, heat a frying pan over medium heat.
7. While it's heating up, brush the eggplant slices on both sides with olive oil.
8. Pan fry them in batches until they are lightly charred on both sides.
9. In a large oven dish, spread a little of the tomato sauce over the bottom.
10. Top the sauce with a layer of eggplant slices.
11. Spoon over this a bit more sauce.
12. Next sprinkle over the sauce a little of the goat cheese, oregano, basil, and salt.
13. Repeat this process until you have several layers of eggplant and sauce.
14. Finish the top layer with the last of the tomato sauce.
15. Bake the lasagna for 30-40 minutes, or until the top is crisp and golden.
16. Let it cool for 10 minutes before serving.

Per serving: Calories: 251 Protein: 9g Carbs: 20g Fiber: 8g Sugar: 14g Fat: 17g

Spanish Potato Omelet

SERVES 2 / PREP TIME: 5 MINUTES / COOK TIME: 40 MINUTES

A slow cooked chunky omelet, typical of a Spanish tapas dish.

---

10 egg whites
salt to taste
1 tbsp olive oil
2 zucchinis, finely chopped
4 roasted red peppers, drained and
finely chopped
1 tbsp garlic infused oil
1 white potato, peeled, boiled and
sliced

1 cup fresh spinach, washed
1 tbsp dried oregano
4 tbsp chives, chopped
1 tbsp olive oil

---

1. Whisk the egg whites lightly in a bowl.
2. Season them with the salt.
3. Now heat the oil in a large frying pan.
4. Add the zucchinis.
5. Sauté them gently for about 10 minutes, or until softened.
6. Let the zucchini cool a little.
7. Pour them in with the egg whites.
8. Now add the roasted peppers to the eggs along with the garlic oil and more salt and pepper.
9. In the hot pan, cook the potato slices for 5-10 minutes.
10. Pour the egg mixture into the pan and cover it with a lid.
11. Turn down the burner to the lowest heat setting.
12. Let it cook without disturbing for 15-20 minutes.
13. When it is cooked through, serve the omelet with the spinach, oregano, and chives dressed in the remaining olive oil.

Hint: Make sure the omelet is cooked through (a knife should pull out clean from the centre.

Per serving: Calories: 475 Protein: 26g Carbs: 48g Fiber: 9g Sugar: 21g Fat: 22g

Cheesy Zucchini & Lemon Risotto

SERVES 4 / PREP TIME: 10 MINUTES / COOK TIME: 35 MINUTES

This delicious take on risotto will have you wanting to make it again!

---

4 zucchinis
olive oil cooking spray
½ cup risotto rice
1 lemon, zested and juiced
4 cups hot low sodium vegetable stock
¼ cup feta cheese, crumbled
2 tbsp cashew milk

---

1. Grate 2 of the zucchinis with a cheese grater into a bowl or on a plate.
2. Dice 2 the other two zucchinis.
3. Spray a skillet with olive oil spray.
4. Add the grated zucchini and the rice.
5. Bump up the heat a bit and stir for 1-2 minutes.
6. Add the lemon juice and a ladle of the hot stock.
7. Bring this to a boil over medium-high heat while stirring constantly.
8. When the liquid has just about been absorbed, add another ladle of stock.
9. Keep cooking like this for 20-25 minutes, or until the rice is just tender and creamy.
10. Stir in the feta cheese and cashew milk.
11. Cover the skillet with a lid or baking sheet.
12. Set it aside for 5 minutes while you cook the remaining zucchini.
13. Spray a small frying pan with the olive oil spray.
14. Add the diced zucchini.
15. Sauté it over high heat for 2-3 minutes, or until golden and just softened.
16. Divide the risotto among 4 shallow bowls or plates.
17. Sprinkle the diced zucchini and lemon zest over the bowls to serve.

Per serving: Calories: 129 Protein: 5g Carbs: 21g Sugar: 9g Fat: 3g

Zucchini Shepherd's Pie

SERVES 2 / PREP TIME: 10 MINUTES / COOK TIME: 1 HOUR

You don't miss the meat in this delicious zucchini version of traditional shepherd's pie!

1 tbsp olive oil
2 zucchinis, diced
2 carrots, diced
1 stalk celery, chopped
2 bay leaves
1 tbsp dried thyme
1 tbsp chopped chives
2 cups low FODMAP vegetable stock
2 tbsp tomato paste

water for boiling potatoes
2 cups white potatoes, peeled and diced
1 cup rice milk
salt to taste

1. Preheat the oven to 375 degrees.
2. To make the sauce, heat the olive oil in a pan.
3. In the warm oil, sauté the vegetables for 10 minutes, or until soft and golden.
4. Stir in the herbs and chives.
5. Now pour the stock over the vegetables.
6. Simmer this for 20 minutes, or until the vegetables are very soft.
7. Now take the pan off the heat and stir in the tomato paste.
8. Meanwhile, place the potatoes into a pan of water.
9. Boil them for about 15 minutes, or until tender.
10. Drain them well.
11. Return the potatoes to the pot and mash them together with the milk and the salt.
12. Pour the vegetable mixture into a deep baking dish.
13. Top them with the mashed potatoes.
14. Use a fork to score the top of the potato mixture, creating ridges.
15. Bake the casserole for 30 minutes, or until the top is golden brown.

Hint: You can add in other low FODMAP veggies to your taste.

Per serving: Calories: 328 Protein: 12g Carbs: 51g Fiber: 9g Sugar: 17g Fat: 10g

STOCKS, SOUPS AND STEWS

Classic Low FODMAP Chicken Stock

SERVES 6 / PREP TIME: 30 MINUTES / COOK TIME: 2 HOURS

This scrumptious chicken stock is great to have on hand year round!

2-3 lb whole chicken, cut apart at the thighs, breasts and legs
2 celery stalks with leaves, diced
2 medium carrots, chopped
2 bay leaves

½ tsp dried parsley
½ tsp dried oregano
¼ tsp dried basil
1 dash pink Himalayan sea salt
8 cups cold water

1. Place all the ingredients in a heavy pot.
2. Bring the stock to a boil.
3. Reduce the heat and skim any foam off the top.
4. Cover the stock and simmer it for 2 hours.
5. After it is done simmering, gently remove the chicken from the broth.
6. Set it aside.
7. Strain the rest of the broth into a glass jar or bowl.
8. Discard the vegetables and seasonings.
9. Refrigerate the broth for 8 hours or overnight.
10. Once cooled, you can skim the fat from the surface.

Hint: Keep this stock in an airtight container in the fridge for 2-3 days or the freezer for 2-3 weeks to use in future recipes. Portion up first to make individual servings easier.

Per serving: Calories: 128 Protein: 8g Carbs: 14g Sugar: 6g Fat: 4g

Low FODMAP Vegetable Stock

SERVES 6 / PREP TIME: 30 MINUTES / COOK TIME: 2 HOURS

This refreshing broth is perfect as a rainy day soup or as an addition to recipes.

2 stalks celery, roughly chopped
6 large carrots, roughly chopped
2 turnips, roughly chopped
3 bay leaves
1 bunch fresh parsley, washed and roughly chopped
2 sprigs fresh rosemary
2 sprigs fresh thyme
1 sprig fresh oregano

1 bunch fresh green onions, chopped (green tips only)
5 whole white peppercorns
1 pinch of salt
4 litres cold water

1. In a large soup pot, bring all the ingredients to a boil.
2. Reduce the heat to a simmer and cook, uncovered, for 2 hours.
3. Occasionally skim the surface to remove any foam that rises.
4. Once it's done cooking, pour the broth through a wire mesh strainer into a glass bowl or jar.
5. Discard the vegetables and herbs.
6. Allow the broth to cool. .

Hint: Keep this stock in an airtight container in the fridge for 2-3 days or the freezer for 2-3 weeks to use in future recipes. Portion up first to make individual servings easier.

Per serving: Calories: 41 Protein: 1g Carbs: 9g Fiber: 3g Sugar: 4g Fat: 0g

Low FODMAP Seafood Stock

SERVES 8 / PREP TIME: 10 MINUTES / COOK TIME: 1 HOUR

This simple stock is good to have around to make recipes interesting!

3 lb fish bones, including heads
6 cups water
1 large carrot, chopped
3 celery stalks, including the leafy top, sliced
1 dash salt

1. Place the fish bones in the water and bring it to a boil.
2. Simmer the bones for 20 minutes.
3. Now pour the water through a wire mesh strainer into another container.
4. Return the stock to the pan and add the vegetables and seasoning.
5. Bring it to a boil.
6. Turn down the heat and simmer the stock again for 45 minutes.
7. Strain it one last time into bowls or jars.
8. Once it has cooled down, you can store it in the fridge or freezer in small quantities.

Hint: Keep this stock in an airtight container in the fridge for 2-3 days or the freezer for 2-3 weeks to use in future recipes. Portion up first to make individual servings easier.

Per serving: Calories: 39 Protein: 4g Carbs: 2g Sugar: 1g Fat: 1g

Sweet Collard Green Stew

SERVES 4 / PREP TIME: 5 MINUTES / COOK TIME: 50 MINUTES

This one-pot stew is enough to fill you up without any sides!

1 tbsp olive oil
1 tsp smoked paprika
1 tsp cumin
6 medium carrots, sliced
1/4 cup water
6 cups dandelion or collard greens,
loosely packed
1 cup water

1 (15 oz) can diced tomatoes, no salt
added
1 (6 oz) can tomato paste, no salt added
3 tbsp low sodium soy sauce or tamari
3 tbsp fresh lemon juice
1 tbsp pure maple syrup
1 tsp salt
1/2 tsp dried oregano

1. Add the oil to a large cooking pot.
2. Add the paprika and cumin.
3. Turn the heat on to medium.
4. Add the carrots and the 1/4 cup water.
5. Put a lid on the pot and let it cook about 10 minutes, stirring occasionally.
6. Stem the greens while the carrots cook.
7. Stir in the rest of the ingredients.
8. Raise the heat to medium-high.
9. Now cover the pot and bring the stew to a boil.
10. Turn the heat down to medium.
11. Uncover the stew and let it simmer about 30-35 minutes.
12. When it's done simmering, serve the stew in bowls.

Per serving: Calories: 324 Protein: 12g Carbs: 58g Fiber: 13g Sugar: 16 Fat: 6g

Creamy Carrot and Potato Bisque

SERVES 4 / PREP TIME: 5 MINUTES / COOK TIME: 30 MINUTES

This bisque is made creamy by the softened potatoes and carrots.

---

2 medium potatoes
2 large carrots
1 1/2 tbsp fresh cilantro, loosely chopped
1 tbsp garlic infused oil
1 tbsp olive oil
1/2 cup green onions (green tips only), sliced

3 cups low FODMAP chicken stock/ vegetable stock
1 tbsp olive oil
1 tbsp dried oregano
1/2 cup unsweetened light coconut milk
salt to taste

---

1. Peel and cut the potatoes and carrots into small pieces.
2. Roughly chop the fresh cilantro.
3. Reserve a few pinches for garnish later.
4. Place the garlic infused oil and olive oil in a large saucepan.
5. Over low heat, cook the green onions for 1 to 2 minutes, stirring occasionally.
6. Next, add the potatoes and carrots to the saucepan.
7. Cook the vegetables over low heat for 5 minutes, stirring occasionally.
8. Add the stock to the saucepan.
9. Turn up the heat to medium-high and bring the soup to a rolling boil.
10. Put the lid on the saucepan and allow the soup to simmer for 10 to 15 minutes, or until the vegetables are tender.
11. Meanwhile, heat the olive oil in a skillet.
12. Add the fresh cilantro and cook it for one minute, then remove it from the heat.
13. Add this to the soup.
14. Once the vegetables are tender, remove the soup from the heat and let it cool for 10 minutes.
15. Transfer the soup to a food processor or blender, in batches if needed, and process the soup until smooth.
16. Rinse out the soup pot and then return the soup to it.
17. Over low heat, mix in the milk and season it with a few grinds of salt to taste.
18. Serve the soup warm with a sprinkle of fresh cilantro.

Per serving: Calories: 193 Protein: 6g Carbs: 18g Sugar: 2g Fat: 13g

Roasted Pepper and Parsnip Soup

SERVES 4 / PREP TIME: 10 MINUTES / COOK TIME: 35 MINUTES

The sweetness of the peppers and parsnips is released during the roasting process of this delectable soup recipe.

2 medium parsnips, peeled & chopped
2 large carrots, peeled and chopped
2 red bell peppers, seeded and cut into strips
1 tbsp coconut oil
salt and pepper to taste
4 cups low FODMAP vegetable stock
1 (15 oz) can diced tomatoes
1 tbsp garlic infused olive oil

1 tbsp paprika
3 tbsp fresh parsley, torn

1. Preheat the oven to 400 degrees.
2. Place the parsnips, carrots, and red peppers on a baking sheet.
3. Drizzle in the oil and season the vegetables with the salt and pepper.
4. Toss this mixture so that the veggies are well coated with oil.
5. Place the sheet in the oven and roast it for 20 to 25 minutes, or until golden and soft.
6. Toss the mixture once while cooking.
7. Once the veggies are roasted, transfer them to a blender.
8. Add half of the stock and the tomatoes to the blender.
9. Blend everything together until smooth.
10. Transfer the soup back into the large saucepan.
11. Place the saucepan over medium heat.
12. Stir into the soup the other half of the stock, the garlic infused oil, and the paprika.
13. Season it with more salt and pepper.
14. Allow the soup to heat through for 10 minutes.
15. Serve the soup with parsley sprinkled on top.

Per serving: Calories: 188 Protein: 5g Carbs: 27g Fiber: 8g Sugar: 12g Fat: 8g

Slow Cooker Chicken Soup

SERVES 4 / PREP TIME: 10 MINUTES / COOK TIME: 6 HOURS

This classic dish tastes wonderful after cooking all day—and smells good too!

---

cooking spray
1 lb skinless chicken breasts
2 large carrots, peeled & chopped
2 parsnips, peeled and chopped
1/2 cup chives (green tips only), finely chopped
2 tbsp garlic infused oil
1 tbsp fresh lemon juice
1/2 tsp dried thyme
1/2 tsp dried rosemary

1/2 tsp dried oregano
2 dried bay leaves
4 cups low FODMAP chicken stock
salt to taste
3 tbsp fresh parsley, finely chopped
1 tbsp fresh cilantro, chopped

---

1. Spray the slow cooker dish with cooking spray.
2. Line the bottom of the slow cooker with the chicken breasts. Cover them with the carrots, parsnips, chives, garlic infused oil, fresh lemon juice, thyme, rosemary, oregano, and bay leaves.
3. Cover everything with the low FODMAP chicken stock.
4. Season it with the salt to taste.
5. Place the lid on the slow cooker.
6. Cook it on low heat for 6 to 7 hours.
7. Just before serving, shred the chicken breasts using two forks.
8. Dish the hot chicken soup into bowls and sprinkle them with the parsley and cilantro.

Per serving: Calories: 276 Protein: 32g Carbs: 20g Fiber: 4g Sugar: 6g Fat: 8g

Quick Oriental Chicken Soup

SERVES 4 / PREP TIME: 5 MINUTES / COOK TIME: 30 MINUTES

This tasty Oriental-flavored chicken soup will comfort you on sick days.

---

1 tbsp olive oil
2 (5 oz) chicken breasts, sliced
salt to taste
2 cups low FODMAP chicken stock
1 tsp powdered ginger
½ tsp turmeric
1 tbsp sliced chives (green ends only),
sliced
½ cup fresh spinach leaves
1 tbsp low sodium soy sauce

1 tsp fish sauce
5 large tomatoes, halved
7 oz rice noodles, cooked

---

1. Heat the oil in a large pot over medium-high heat.
2. Add the chicken breast slices and season them with the salt.
3. Sauté them for 15-20 minutes, or until golden-brown and cooked through.
4. In a different pan, bring the stock to a boil.
5. To the stock, add the ginger, turmeric, chives, spinach, soy sauce, fish sauce, and tomatoes.
6. Reduce the heat and allow it to simmer for 4-5 minutes, or until heated through.
7. Add to the stock the cooked chicken and rice noodles.
8. Continue to heat until the mixture is warmed through.
9. Serve in bowls.

Hint: Check that the juices of the chicken run clear when pierced in the thickest part.

Per serving: Calories: 323 Protein: 21g Carbs: 44g Fiber: 4g Sugar: 5g Fat: 7g

Rich Tomato Bisque

SERVES 2 / PREP TIME: 5 MINUTES / COOK TIME: 30 MINUTES

Potatoes are the secret to this creamy yet healthy tomato soup.

3 tbsp olive oil	5 tbsp tomato paste
2 celery stalks, chopped	1 tsp dried oregano
2 small carrots, peeled and chopped	2 tbsp coconut sugar
1 large white potato, peeled and diced	3 tbsp red wine vinegar
4 bay leaves	4 cups tomatoes, diced
	1 cup low FODMAP chicken stock

1. Add the oil, celery, carrots, potato, and bay leaves to a large pot over medium heat.
2. Stir in the tomato paste, oregano, sugar, vinegar, tomatoes, and stock.
3. Cover the soup and let it simmer for 25 minutes, or until the potato is tender.
4. Remove the bay leaves.
5. Next, purée the soup with a stick blender until it is very smooth.
6. Ladle into 2 bowls to serve.

Hint: If you don't have a stick blender, ladle the soup into a blender in batches.

Per serving: Calories: 495 Protein: 12g Carbs: 68g Fiber: 13g Sugar: 24g Fat: 22g

Puréed Morrocan Zucchini Soup

SERVES 2 / PREP TIME: 5 MINUTES / COOK TIME: 35 MINUTES

This creamy soup is marked by the North African flavors of cinnamon and turmeric.

1 tbsp olive oil
2 stalks celery, chopped
2 zucchinis, sliced
2 cups tomatoes, diced
2 tbsp coconut flour
½ tsp turmeric
½ tsp ground cumin

2 cups low FODMAP vegetable stock

1. Heat the olive oil in a large pan.
2. Add the celery and zucchini.
3. Cook them for 5 minutes over medium heat, stirring occasionally.
4. Add the tomatoes and coconut flour.
5. Cook for 2 minutes while stirring.
6. Add the turmeric, cumin, and stock.
7. Cover and simmer the soup for 30 minutes.
8. Purée the soup with a stick blender until it is very smooth.
9. Ladle into 2 bowls to serve.

Hint: If you don't have a stick blender, ladle the soup into a blender in batches.

Per serving: Calories: 155 Protein: 3g Carbs: 16g Sugar: 5g Fat: 8g

Creamy Carrot and Potato Soup

SERVES 2 / PREP TIME: 10 MINUTES / COOK TIME: 1 HOURS

This delightful creamy soup is sure to be a crowd pleaser!

---

3 tbsp olive oil
2 celery stalks, chopped
2 carrots, sliced
1 white potato, peeled and diced
1 dried bay leaf
1/2 tsp dried oregano

2 cups tomatoes, diced
1 tbsp coconut sugar
1 tbsp red wine vinegar
2 cups low FODMAP vegetable stock
½ cup cashew milk

---

1. Add the oil and celery to a large pot.
2. Sautee the celery gently until it has softened, about 5 minutes.
3. Add the carrots and potato.
4. Cook for 3 more minutes.
5. Now add all the remaining ingredients except the milk.
6. Bring the soup to a simmer.
7. Cover the soup and let it simmer for 30 minutes.
8. After this, allow it to simmer uncovered for 20-30 minutes.
9. Remove the bay leaves.
10. Use a stick blender or regular blender to puree the soup into a creamy consistency.
11. Add the cashew milk and stir well.
12. Ladle into 2 bowls to serve.

Per serving: Calories: 353 Protein: 4 Carbs: 38 Sugar: 17 Fat: 22

Roasted Bell Pepper Bisque

SERVES 4 / PREP TIME: 10 MINUTES / COOK TIME: 45 MINUTES

The rich flavors of bell peppers and eggplant shine through in this creamy bisque.

2 large tomatoes, halved
1 red bell pepper, roughly chopped
1 yellow bell pepper, roughly chopped
2 celery stalks, diced
1 eggplant, roughly chopped
2 tbsp coconut oil
1 tbsp balsamic vinegar
2 tbsp coconut sugar
1 tsp dried thyme

1 tbsp dried oregano
1 tsp dried basil
2 cups low FODMAP vegetable Stock
salt to taste

1. Preheat the oven to 400 degrees.
2. Peel and roughly chop the vegetables.
3. Place them together into a roasting pan.
4. In a separate bowl, mix together the coconut oil, vinegar, sugar, thyme, oregano, and basil.
5. Drizzle the mixture over the vegetables.
6. Cover and transfer the roasting pan to the oven.
7. Roast the vegetables for 35 minutes, or until they are tender and golden brown.
8. Heat the vegetable stock in your stockpot.
9. Add the roasted vegetables to the soup.
10. Once it is boiling, reduce the heat and simmer for 10 minutes.
11. Turn off the heat and let the soup cool down for a few minutes.
12. Purée the ingredients with a hand blender in the stockpot, or puree them in batches in a blender.
13. Return the soup to the pan.
14. Season it to taste with the salt.
15. Ladle into 4 bowls to serve.

Per serving: Calories: 151 Protein: 4g Carbs: 20g Fiber: 7g Sugar: 12g Fat: 8g

Pumpkin Sage Bisque

SERVES 4 / PREP TIME: 15 MINUTES / COOK TIME: 1 HOUR 15 MINUTES

The delicious blend of pumpkin and sage makes a perfect autumn dinner!

1 (5 lb) pumpkin, gutted (use canned alterantively
1 tbsp coconut oil
½ tsp cumin
½ tsp tumeric
salt to taste
6 cups low FODMAP vegetable stock
8 fresh sage Leaves

1. Using a sharp knife and a spoon, carefully hollow out the pumpkin, removing the flesh and setting it aside.
2. Roughly chop the scooped-out pumpkin flesh.
3. Heat a pan and add the oil.
4. Add the pumpkin flesh, cumin, turmeric, and salt.
5. Increase the heat to medium and cover it with the lid.
6. Cook for 40-45 minutes, stirring occasionally to prevent it from burning, until the pumpkin is cooked through.
7. Pour in the stock and bring it to a rolling boil.
8. Remove the soup from the heat and allow it to cool slightly.
9. Use a stick blender, or transfer the soup to a food processor in batches, and blend until smooth.
10. Return the soup to the pan.
11. Add the sage leaves.
12. Bring it to a low simmer and cook for another 30 minutes.
13. Skim out the sage leaves with a slotted spoon and ladle it into bowls.

Per serving: Calories: 104 Protein: 5g Carbs: 15g Fiber: 3g Sugar: 4g Fat: 4g

Fresh Parsley & Potato Turkey Stew

SERVES 2 / PREP TIME: 10 MINUTES / COOK TIME: 1 HOUR 15 MINUTES

This unique stew is perfect for any winter evening meal!

1 tbsp olive oil
2 (6 oz) turkey breasts
salt and pepper to taste
2 stalks celery, diced
2 carrots, diced
1 tsp dried oregano
1 tsp dried cilantro
2 cups low FODMAP chicken stock
2 medium white potatoes, peeled and
cubed
1 bunch fresh parsley, roughly chopped

1. Heat a stock pot over high heat.
2. Add the oil.
3. While the oil is heating, season the turkey with the salt and pepper.
4. Add it to the pan and brown it, stirring on each side, about 7-8 minutes.
5. Turn the heat down to medium and add the celery, carrots, oregano, and cilantro.
6. Pour in the stock, mixing well.
7. Reduce the heat, cover, and simmer for 1 hour, stirring occasionally.
8. Once the turkey is cooked, remove it from the stew and leave to one side to cool slightly.
9. Add the potatoes to the stew.
10. Cover the stew again and continue to cook it for 20 minutes, or until the potatoes are tender.
11. Meanwhile, shred the meat after it has cooled down.
12. Add the meat back to the pan with the cooked potatoes and stew mixture.
13. Mix well.
14. Once you are ready to serve the stew, stir in the chopped parsley.
15. Serve it hot.

Hint: Use dinner forks or meat claws to shred the turkey meat.

Per serving: Calories: 429 Protein: 44g Carbs: 42g Fiber: 6g Sugar: 3g Fat: 9g

Gluten Free Paprika Chicken Goulash

SERVES 4 / PREP TIME: 10 MINUTES / COOK TIME: 35 MINUTES

This healthy goulash is served over rice noodles for a delicious dinner!

2 tbsp olive oil
2 carrots, diced
2 stalks celery, diced
2 medium white potatoes, peeled and diced
4 (5 oz) skinless chicken breasts, diced
1 tbsp smoked paprika
1 tbsp golden flax meal
4 cups low FODMAP chicken stock
1 tbsp tomato paste

salt to taste
4 large tomatoes, diced
1 red bell pepper, seeded and diced
2 tbsp green onion (tips only), sliced
1 (8 oz) package rice noodles, cooked

1. Heat half the oil in a large frying pan.
2. Gently sauté the carrots and celery for 5 minutes, or until they are softened.
3. Add the potatoes and sauté for 2 more minutes.
4. Remove the vegetables from the pan with a slotted spoon and set them to the side.
5. Add the remaining oil to the pan and sear the diced chicken on all sides
6. Return the vegetables to the pan and sprinkle in the paprika and flax meal.
7. Cook this for 2 minutes, stirring frequently.
8. Gradually stir in the stock, tomato paste, and salt.
9. Bring this to a boil, stirring occasionally, then lower the heat.
10. Add the diced tomatoes to the soup and simmer for 20 minutes.
11. In a saucepan, blanch the bell pepper in boiling water for 4 minutes.
12. Drain it and add the pepper to the soup.
13. Cook it for 5-10 minutes, or until the chicken is tender.
14. Pour the goulash into a warm serving dish, sprinkle it with the sliced green onions, and serve it on a bed of rice noodles.

Per serving: Calories: 622 Protein: 42g Carbs: 82g Fiber: 9g Sugar: 9g Fat: 14g

Sweet Spiced Stove Top Moroccan Chicken

SERVES 2 / PREP TIME: 10 MINUTES / COOK TIME: 30 MINUTES

The maple syrup in this recipe complements Moroccan spices for a delectable chicken dish.

1 tbsp olive oil
4 (5 oz) skinless chicken breasts
1 tsp cumin
1 tsp ground ginger
1 tsp ground cumin
peel from half a lemon, chopped
3 tsp chopped fresh cilantro
2 tsp chopped fresh parsley

1 (15 oz) can diced tomatoes
1 tbsp pure maple syrup
fresh lime juice to serve

1. Heat the olive oil in a heavy saucepan.
2. Add the chicken breasts and fry them for 1-2 minutes.
3. Add the cumin, ginger, and cumin.
4. 2-3 minutes, or until golden.
5. Add the lemon peel, cilantro, parsley, and the blanched olives.
6. Next, add the tomatoes and the maple syrup to cover the chicken.
7. Return the pan to a boil.
8. Reduce the heat, cover, and simmer on a low heat for about 35 minutes.
9. Serve on plates with fresh lime juice squeezed over the top of each breast.

Per serving: Calories: 275 Protein: 33g Carbs: 8g Fiber: 2g Sugar: 6g Fat: 12g

Potato and Paprika Chicken Potage

SERVES 8 / PREP TIME: 5 MINUTES / COOK TIME: 25 MINUTES

This hearty soup makes a good mid-week evening meal.

---

2 tbsp olive oil
8 (5 oz) boneless skinless chicken breasts, halved
8 medium white potatoes, peeled and cubed
1 tbsp tomato paste
2 tsp paprika
2 tbsp red wine vinegar
1/3 cup sherry

1 tbsp garlic infused oil
4 cups low FODMAP chicken stock
1 tbsp chopped green onions (green tips only)
salt to taste
1 tsp dried oregano

---

1. Heat half the oil in a large pot over medium heat.
2. Add the chicken to the pan.
3. Fry it for about 4 minutes, or until it is browned all over.
4. Remove the chicken and set it aside.
5. Add the potatoes and tomato paste to the pan and cook it all for 1 minute.
6. Stir in the paprika, vinegar, sherry, garlic oil, and stock.
7. Bring to a boil and allow the liquid to reduce for 2 minutes.
8. Return the chicken to the pan, cover, and simmer it for 10 minutes.
9. Add the green onions.
10. Stir well and simmer the soup with the lid off for another 8 minutes, or until the sauce is thickened and the potatoes and chicken are cooked through.

Per serving: Calories: 407 Protein: 39g Carbs: 40g Fiber: 5g Sugar: 2g Fat: 10g

Sweet and Spiced North African Fish Stew

SERVES 4 / PREP TIME: 5 MINUTES / COOK TIME: 20 MINUTES

This light, tasty stew is ready in a flash!

---

1 tbsp olive oil
1 tsp ground ginger
1 tsp ground cumin
1 tsp turmeric
1 cinnamon stick
1 (15 oz) can diced tomatoes
1 tbsp chopped green onions (green tips only), sliced
1 pinch pink Himalayan sea salt

1 lb white cod, cut into chunks
2 tsp pure maple syrup
1 tbsp fresh cilantro leaves

---

1. Heat the olive oil in a stock pot over medium heat.
2. Add the ginger, cumin, turmeric, and cinnamon stick and cook for two minutes, stirring regularly.
3. Add the tomatoes, green onions, and salt.
4. Cook, stirring frequently, for 10 minutes.
5. Add the cod and simmer for five minutes, or until the fish is almost cooked through and tender.
6. Add the syrup and cook for 2-3 more minutes.
7. To serve, ladle the stew into bowls and garnish with fresh cilantro leaves.

Per serving: Calories: 132 Protein: 17g Carbs: 6g Fiber: 2g Sugar: 4g Fat: 4g

Savory Pumpkin & Spinach Stew

SERVES 4 / PREP TIME: 10 MINUTES / COOK TIME: 45 MINUTES

This light tomato-based stew makes a lovely vegetarian entrée.

---

2 tbsp coconut oil
1 tsp whole cumin seeds
1 (7 lb) pumpkin, peeled and cut into medium chunks
2 (15 oz) cans diced tomatoes
1 cup water
1 tbsp chopped scallions (green tips only)

2 cups fresh spinach, washed and roughly chopped
1 tbsp fresh parsley, chopped

---

1. Heat the oil in a stock pot with a lid over medium heat.
2. Stir in the cumin seeds until fragrant, about 1 minute.
3. Next add the pumpkin, tomatoes, and water.
4. Stir, cover, and bring to a boil.
5. Uncover the pot and let it simmer for 15 minutes.
6. Simmer for another 15 minutes, stirring frequently this time.
7. Next, stir in the scallions and spinach.
8. Return the stew to a boil and simmer with the lid on, stirring occasionally, for 8-10 minutes, or until the spinach is cooked.
9. Serve piping hot and garnish with the chopped parsley.

Per serving: Calories: 159 Protein: 4g Carbs: 23g Fiber: 8g Sugar: 8g Fat: 8g

Zucchini & Spinach Soup

SERVES 4 / PREP TIME: 5 MINUTES / COOK TIME: 35 MINUTES

Fresh and tasty!

---

3 zucchinis, diced
2 medium carrots, diced
1 large white potato, diced
water to cook the vegetables
1 cup fresh spinach
salt to taste
1 tsp dried basil
1 tbsp olive oil

---

1. In a large saucepan, add the zucchini, carrots, and potato.
2. Pour in enough water to cover the vegetables.
3. Bring to a gentle boil and cook over medium heat for 30 minutes, or until the vegetables are mushy.
4. Purée the soup in a blender or in the pot with a stick blender.
5. Season the soup with the salt, and basil.
6. Stir in the spinach, cover, and simmer for 5 more minutes.
7. Just before serving, stir in the olive oil.

Per serving: Calories: 141 Protein: 4g Carbs: 24g Fiber: 5g Sugar: 6g Fat: 4g

Garbanzo Bean and Pepper Stew

SERVES 1 / PREP TIME: 5 MINUTES / COOK TIME: 30 MINUTES

Hearty and wholesome.

---

1 tbsp garlic infused olive oil
1 large carrot, peeled and sliced thinly
1 red bell pepper, seeded and chopped
1 large tomato, chopped
1/2 cup dry red wine
1 tsp paprika
1 pinch cinnamon
1 tsp dried oregano
1/4 tsp salt

1/2 cup quinoa
3/4 cup water
1/2 cup canned garbanzo beans, drained and rinsed
1/4 cup sliced chives (green tips only)
1 tbsp fresh cilantro, chopped
1/2 tbsp fresh lemon juice

---

1. Heat the garlic oil in a large pot.
2. Add the carrot, bell pepper, tomato, wine, paprika, cinnamon, oregano, and salt.
3. Bring all of this to a boil.
4. Once the mixture boils, reduce the heat to a simmer and cook, covered, for 15 minutes.
5. Meanwhile, in a small saucepan, bring the quinoa and water to a boil.
6. Once it is boiling, reduce the heat to low, cover, and let it cook for 12 minutes.
7. After the stew has been cooking for 15 minutes, add the chickpeas, chives, cilantro, and lemon juice.
8. Heat the soup through.
9. Divide the cooked quinoa and stew between two bowls to serve.

Per serving: Calories: 399 Protein: 12g Carbs: 54g Fiber: 11g Sugar: 1g Fat: 11g

Spiced Chicken & Brown Rice Soup

SERVES 4 / PREP TIME: 10 MINUTES / COOK TIME: 50 MINUTES

If you like chicken and rice, you'll love this cinnamon and turmeric version!

---

4 (5 oz) boneless skinless chicken breasts
8 cups water
8 fresh thyme sprigs
1/2 tbsp turmeric
1/2 tsp ground cinnamon
1 large celery stalk with leaves, chopped
salt to taste
1 tsp dried oregano

1/2 cup thinly sliced carrots
1 1/2 cups cooked brown rice

---

1. Add the chicken, water, 6 of the sprigs of thyme, turmeric, cinnamon, celery, and salt to a medium stock pot over high heat.
2. Bring the mixture to boil for about 20 minutes.
3. Lower to a rolling simmer for a further 20 minutes.
4. Check the chicken to ensure it is cooked throughout.
5. Add the carrots to the broth.
6. Turn the heat back on to high and boil for 5 minutes, or until the carrots are tender.
7. Add in the cooked rice and reduce the heat to a simmer.
8. Remove the sprigs of thyme with a slotted spoon.
9. Pour the soup in a large serving bowl and add fresh thyme as a garnish.

Hint: The chicken should be piping hot and completely white through the centre once cooked.

Per serving: Calories: 263 Protein: 34g Carbs: 19 gFiber: 2g Sugar: 1g Fat: 4g

Hearty Turkey Chili

SERVES 4 / PREP TIME: 5 MINUTES / COOK TIME: 45 MINUTES

This chili is full of flavorful spices and ingredients to make it unforgettable!

2 cups water
3/4 cup crushed tomatoes
2 tbsp garlic infused oil, divided
1 lb lean ground turkey
1 green bell pepper, seeded and diced
1 1/4 tsp ground cumin
salt to taste
1 cup canned chickpeas, drained and rinsed

4 green onions (green tips only), diced

1. Bring the water to a boil in a pan.
2. Add the crushed tomatoes and half of the garlic-infused oil to the water.
3. Transfer this mixture to the bowl of a blender and puree, or puree in the bowl using an immersion blender.
4. Meanwhile, add the other tablespoon of garlic oil to a large Dutch oven or stock pot.
5. Add the turkey and cook until it is brown.
6. Add the bell pepper and cook 5 more minutes, or until the pepper is softened.
7. Add the cumin, salt, and tomatoes to the pot.
8. Bring it to a boil.
9. Then reduce the heat to medium-low and simmer for 30 minutes.
10. After 30 minutes, add the chickpeas and green onions.
11. Cook for 5 to 10 more minutes before serving.

Per serving: Calories: 280 Protein: 30g Carbs: 18g Fiber: 5g Sugar: 5g Fat: 10g

SIDES, SALADS, SNACKS AND SAUCES

Baba Ganoush Dip

SERVES: 8 / PREP TIME: 15 MINUTES / COOK TIME: 45 MINUTES

You'll love this smoky dip with crudites!

---

1 medium eggplant (about 1 pound)
1 cup cooked or canned chickpeas,
rinsed and drained
1 tbsp garlic infused oil
2 tbsp tahini

1/4 tsp salt
1/4 cup fresh lemon juice
1 tbsp finely chopped fresh cilantro

---

1. Preheat broiler to a medium- low heat.
2. Prick eggplant in several places with a fork and layer on an oven tray.
3. Broil on the top shelf for 45 minutes. turning every 10 minutes or so, until eggplant is charred all over.
4. Remove and cover very loosely with foil to allow to sweat.
5. When cool, remove the skin and transfer pulp to a blender or food processor. Add all remaining ingredients except cilantro and puree until very smooth.
6. Transfer to serving bowl and sprinkle with cilantro.

Per serving: Calories: 69 Protein: 2g Carbs: 8g Fiber: 2g Sugar: 2g Fat: 3g

Parsley & Cumin Lentils

SERVES: 2 / PREP TIME: 5 MINUTES / COOK TIME: 30 MINUTES

Lentils can be enjoyed in small quantities and are a great source of protein.

---

1 cup canned/dry red lentils
1 tbsp fresh parsley
1 tbsp garlic infused oil
1 tsp olive oil
1/2 tsp cumin

1/2 tsp. turmeric
1/4 cup water

1 cup spinach, washed

---

1. If using dry lentils, soak in warm water overnight before using.
2. If using canned, simply drain before using.
3. Whisk together the garlic oil and parsley and place to one side.
4. Heat the olive oil in a small pan over a medium heat and add the lentils.
5. Now sprinkle over the cumin and turmeric, pour in the water, cover and lower the heat.
6. Allow to steam for 20-30 minutes (keep an eye on the water to make sure the lentils don't burn).
7. When the water has been soaked up and the lentils are soft, remove and serve on a bed of spinach and drizzle over the lemon dressing.

Per serving: Calories: 381 Protein: 25g Carbs: 56g Fiber: 22g Sugar: 5g Fat: 8g

Pineapple & Tomato Salsa

SERVES: 2 / PREP TIME: 5 MINUTES / COOK TIME: 30 MINUTES

So simple yet delicious.

---

4 ripe large tomatoes
1 tbsp fresh lime juice
1/4 cup pineapple, diced
A pinch of salt and pepper

---

1. Preheat broiler to a low heat.
2. Broil tomatoes until lightly chargrilled, turning to cook evenly on all sides.
3. Remove and allow to cool.
4. Chop tomatoes and mix in with the rest of the ingredients!
5. Easy.

Per serving: Calories: 61 Protein: 3g Carbs: 14g Fiber: 4g Sugar: 9g Fat: 1g

Homemade Ketchup

SERVING SIZE: 1 TBSP / PREP TIME: 5 MINUTES / COOK TIME: NA

A homemade version of the shop bought favorite.

12oz tomato paste
½ cup brown sugar
2/3 cup water
4 tbsp. white wine vinegar
½ tsp. sea salt

---

1.   Mix together all of the ingredients until the sugar is completely dissolved.
2.   You can then refrigerate your ketchup for up to 3 to 4 weeks in an airtight container.
3.   Please note this makes approx. 1 cup sauce and nutritional information is based on a serving size of 1 tbsp.

Per serving: Calories: 88 Protein: 2g Carbs: 21g Fiber: 2g Sugar: 18g Fat: 0g

Strawberry Jam

SERVES: 4 / PREP TIME: 5 MINUTES / COOK TIME: 20 MINUTES

Make your own jam and enjoy on toast and crumpets!

---

2 cups strawberries, washed and sliced
1 tbsp. stevia powder
1 tbsp. fresh lemon juice

---

1. Combine all of the ingredients together over a medium heat in a pan.
2. Bring your mixture to the boil, stirring occasionally with a wooden spoon for 5-10 minutes.
3. Mash up the strawberries with your wooden spoon whilst cooking.
4. Reduce the heat down to low and then allow the mixture to simmer for 10 minutes.
5. Transfer the jam to a Mason jar or airtight container.
6. You can then store the contents for up to a week.

Top tip: wash out your old jam jars and save for future homemade jams and sauces. The seal will be broken so make sure you keep anything you store in the fridge for up to 2-3 days.

Per serving: Calories: 23 Protein: 0g Carbs: 6g Fiber: 1g Sugar: 4g Fat: 0g

Classic Pesto Spread

SERVES 4 / PREP TIME: 5 MINUTES / COOK TIME: NA

This fast and easy spread does wonders for any Italian entrée!

1 cup fresh basil, packed
1/4 cup pecan nuts
1/4 cup garlic infused olive oil
1/4 cup feta cheese
1 tsp salt

1. Combine the basil and the pine nuts in a food processor.
2. Pulse until they are coarsely chopped.
3. Slowly add the garlic-infused olive oil in a constant stream while the food processor is on.
4. Add the feta cheese and pulse again until it is well-blended and smooth.
5. Pulse in the salt.
6. Serve immediately, or store in an airtight container and refrigerate until you are ready to use it.

Hint: If freezing, transfer it to an air-tight container and drizzle some olive oil on top. It's also wise to eliminate the cheese initially and add it when you intend to use the pesto.

Per serving: Calories: 203 Protein: 3g Carbs: 2g Fiber: 0g Sugar: 1g Fat: 21g

Homemade Tasty BBQ Sauce

SERVES 6 / PREP TIME: 10 MINUTES / COOK TIME: 10 MINUTES

This delectable homemade BBQ will make you never want to buy it again!

---

2 tbsp cornstarch
1/2 cup cold water
1/2 cup hot water
3 tbsp coconut sugar
1 cup red wine vinegar

1 tbsp garlic infused olive oil
1 tsp salt
1/4 tsp asafoetida powder (garlic & onion replacement)
1/4 tsp liquid smoke

---

1. Mix the cornstarch with the cold water and set aside.
2. In a sauce pan, combine the hot water and sugar, stirring until the sugar is dissolved.
3. Bring this to a boil and cook it for 5 minutes.
4. Stir in the cornstarch and all remaining ingredients.
5. Mix it all together very well.
6. Bring it to a boil, then reduce the heat and simmer, uncovered, for 5 minutes.
7. Remove from the heat and cool it to room temperature.
8. Use the sauce immediately or refrigerate in an airtight container up to 1 week.

Per serving: Calories: 69 Protein: 0g Carbs: 12g Sugar: 9g Fat: 2g

Cheesy Homemade Zucchini Chips

SERVES 4 / PREP TIME: 10 MINUTES / COOK TIME: 1 HOUR

This take on a popular healthy snack will have you making this recipe again and again!

---

2 medium zucchinis, very thinly sliced
2 tsp olive oil
1/2 tbsp hard parmesan cheese, freshly grated
1/4 tsp salt

---

1. Line 4 baking sheets with parchment paper.
2. Preheat the oven to 100 degrees, or its lowest setting.
3. Using a mandolin slicer set to 1/8-inch thickness, slice the zucchini.
4. Place the zucchini slices in a medium bowl and add the olive oil, parmesan cheese, and salt.
5. Toss the bowl to evenly coat each slice of zucchini.
6. Evenly space out the zucchini slices on the baking sheets so that none are overlapping.
7. Bake the zucchini at 100 degrees for 1 hour.
8. Store chips in an air-tight container.

Per serving: Calories: 40 Protein: 1g Carbs: 3g Fiber: 1g Sugar: 2g Fat: 3g

Pumpkin Spice Cookies

SERVES 12 COOKIES / PREP TIME: 10 MINUTES / COOK TIME: 10 MINUTES

These chocolate and pumpkin cookies are so soft, they're like little muffin bites!

1/2 cup melted coconut oil
1/2 cup coconut sugar
1 tsp vanilla extract
6 tbsp pumpkin puree
1 1/2 cup rice flour
1 tsp xanthan gum
1/4 tsp salt
1/2 tsp baking soda
1/4 tsp baking powder

1 pinch sea salt
1/2 cup cocoa powder

1. Preheat the oven to 350 degrees.
2. In a large bowl, mix together the coconut oil, coconut sugar, vanilla extract, and pumpkin puree until smooth.
3. Set this aside while mixing the flour.
4. In another bowl, whisk together the rice flour, xanthan gum, salt, baking soda, baking powder, cinnamon, nutmeg, and salt.
5. Add the flour mixture to the wet ingredients a little bit at a time until everything is combined.
6. Fold in the cocoa powder.
7. If your dough is too sticky to handle at this stage, cover and refrigerate it for at least 10 minutes.
8. Line the baking sheets with parchment paper or grease them.
9. Roll out the dough into little balls about the size of a tablespoon.
10. Place them on the baking sheet.
11. Press down on each ball to flatten them a bit.
12. Bake the cookies for 8-10 minutes.
13. Let them cookies sit to cool on the baking tray for about 5 minutes before transferring them to a cooling rack.

Hint: If you pick up these cookies before they have cooled down, they won't stay together because there is no egg in this recipe.

Per serving: Calories: 192 Protein: 2g Carbs: 26g Sugar: 8g Fat: 10g

Homemade Rice Cakes

SERVES 2 (2 CAKES EACH) / PREP TIME: 5 MINUTES / COOK TIME: 20 MINUTES

Experiment with ingredients to create simply wonderful snacks!

¾ cup basmati rice, pre-boiled
1 beef tomato, finely diced
1/4 cup goats cheese, crumbled
1 tbsp dried mixed herbs
3 egg whites, lightly beaten

---

1. Preheat oven to 400f/200c/ Gas mark 6.
2. Line a muffin sheet with 4 muffin cups.
3. Place the cooled rice, tomatoes, cheese, herbs, pepper, egg whites into a mixing bowl until combined.
4. Then, spoon out your mixture into the prepared pan.
5. Bake the rice cakes for 15 to 20 minutes until they are golden in color and firm.
6. Allow to cool for 5 minutes and then use a knife to ease the edges out.
7. Let them cool for a few more minutes and then serve.

Per serving: Calories: 237 Protein: 15g Carbs: 21g Sugar: 3g Fat: 10g

Mini Chicken Quiches

SERVES 4 / PREP TIME: 5 MINUTES / COOK TIME: 20 MINUTES

Great for on the go lunches!

4 tbsp rice milk
2 tbsp rice flour
4 egg whites
A pinch of salt and pepper
½ red bell pepper, finely diced
1 scallion stem, finely diced (green tip only)

1 tsp dried thyme
1 cup skinless cooked chicken breast, diced

1. Preheat oven to 350f/180c/ Gas mark 4.
2. Line a muffin sheet with 4 muffin cups.
3. Mix the flour and milk together in a mixing bowl.
4. Then, whisk in the eggs along with a pinch of salt and pepper.
5. Whisk until smooth.
6. Mix in the rest of the ingredients.
7. Pour the mixture into the cases evenly, leaving 1/2 cm gap at the top.
8. Bake for 15-20 minutes or until eggs are firm.
9. Remove from the oven and allow to cool before popping them out of their cases (or leave them in and pop them in a lunchbox for later!)

Per serving: Calories: 101 Protein: 15g Carbs: 6gSugar: 2g Fat: 2g

Cucumber & Goats Cheese Rolls

SERVES 6 / PREP TIME: 10 MINUTES / COOK TIME: NA

Quick and healthy snacks.

---

1 large cucumber
3/4 cup soft goat cheese, crumbled
2 tsp garlic infused oil
2 tsp fresh dill, chopped
1/2 tsp dried oregano
1 green onion, sliced (green tips only)
1 pinch sea salt
6 toothpicks

---

1. Wash the cucumber.
2. Cut the cucumber up by trimming the ends and cutting the flesh into 6 1.5 inch slices, cutting lengthwise.
3. In a small bowl, toss the goat cheese with the garlic infused oil, the dill, and the oregano.
4. Place 1 tablespoon of the cheese mixture at the end of each cucumber slice.
5. Garnish the cheese with the green onion slices and the salt.
6. Roll each slice up and pierce it with a toothpick to hold it together.
7. Serve the cucumber rollups on a plate.

Per serving: Calories: 82 Protein: 4g Carbs: 1g Fiber: 0g Sugar: 1g Fat: 7g

Zesty Lime Sweet Potato Fries

SERVES 2 / PREP TIME: 5 MINUTES / COOK TIME: 45 MINUTES

The lime in this recipe enhances these sweet potatoes and gives them a unique flavor.

1 medium sweet potato
1 1/2 tbsp fresh lime juice
2 tsp lime zest
1 tbsp coconut oil, melted
1/2 tsp paprika
salt to taste

1. Preheat the oven to 400 degrees.
2. Slice the sweet potato into fries, in 1/2 inch by 3 inch strips.
3. Add the potato slices to a medium bowl and drizzle them with the lime juice, zest, oil, paprika, and salt.
4. Place the potatoes on a lightly oiled cookie sheet or one lined with parchment paper.
5. Bake them for 35-45 minutes, or until crisp.

Hint: Soften the sweet potato before slicing it by cooking it in the microwave for about 3-4 minutes, being sure to pierce the skin with a fork or knife several times before cooking. Let the potato cool for 30 minutes so you can handle it.

Per serving: Calories: 119 Protein: 1 g Carbs: 14g Fiber: 2g Sugar: 3g Fat: 7g

Quick Tossed Tomatoes and Basil

SERVES 2 / PREP TIME: 5 MINUTES / COOK TIME: NA

This fast and easy salad makes eating healthy a breeze!

2 tbsp garlic infused olive oil
1/4 cup chopped fresh basil
1/2 cup diced Roma tomatoes
salt to taste
1/2 tsp dried oregano

1. Toss together the salad ingredients in a salad bowl.
2. Serve it on plates.

Per serving: Calories: 147 Protein: 1g Carbs: 3g Fiber: 1g Sugar: 1g Fat: 15g

Easy Homemade Oven Fries

SERVES 3 / PREP TIME: 5 MINUTES / COOK TIME: 25 MINUTES

These simple baked potato fries make a great snack or side to a meal!

---

6 small red potatoes, washed
1 tbsp garlic infused oil
1 tbsp olive oil, melted
1 tbsp chopped fresh rosemary
1 tsp paprika
sea salt to taste

---

1. Preheat the oven to 400 degrees.
2. Slice the potatoes into wedges and place them on a cookie sheet.
3. Drizzle them evenly with the oil.
4. Then use a pastry brush to evenly spread the olive oil over the potatoes.
5. Sprinkle the rosemary, paprika, salt, and pepper over the potatoes.
6. Bake for 25 minutes.
7. Turn potatoes halfway through baking to cook them evenly.
8. Remove from the oven and serve.

Per serving: Calories: 235 Protein: 4g Carbs: 37g Fiber: 4g Sugar: 3g Fat: 9g

Mediterranean Quinoa & Sweet Potato Salad

SERVES 4 / PREP TIME: 5 MINUTES / COOK TIME: 25 MINUTES

Crumbled feta with sweet potato salad.

---

1 sweet potato
1 tbsp olive oil
1/2 cup red quinoa
1 cup water
sea salt to taste
1 cup fresh spinach
1/4 cup feta cheese, crumbled

3 tbsp olive oil
1 tbsp balsamic vinegar
1 dash dried oregano
salt to taste

---

1. Preheat the oven to 400 degrees.
2. Cut the sweet potato into cubes and place them on a baking sheet.
3. Drizzle them with the olive oil and place the sheet in in the oven for 20-25 minutes.
4. Meanwhile, rinse the half cup of quinoa in cold water.
5. Combine it with the cup of water and sea salt in a saucepan and bring it to a boil.
6. Turn the heat down and let it simmer for 15 minutes, or until all the water is absorbed.
7. Fluff the quinoa with a fork and set it aside to cool.
8. Now toss together the spinach and feta cheese in a medium bowl.
9. Gently add the cooled sweet potatoes and quinoa to the spinach and feta cheese.
10. Make the dressing by mixing together the rest of the ingredients.
11. Drizzle the dressing over the bowl of quinoa and sweet potato salad.
12. Serve with salad tongs.

Per serving: Calories: 254 Protein: 5g Carbs: 21g Fiber: 3g Sugar: 3g Fat: 17g

Zesty Kale Salad

SERVES 4 / PREP TIME: 5 MINUTES / COOK TIME: 20 MINUTES

This lemony kale salad tossed with quinoa makes a great lunch!

1/4 cup olive oil
1/4 cup apple cider vinegar
1 lemon, juiced and zested
1 tbsp coconut sugar
salt to taste
2 cups chopped kale, de-stemmed
1/2 cup cooked quinoa

1/2 cup red grapes, seedless and halved
1/4 cup crumbled feta cheese

1.
2. To make the vinaigrette, whisk together the olive oil, apple cider vinegar, lemon juice, lemon zest, sugar, salt, and pepper in a small bowl.
3. Set aside the vinaigrette while assembling the salad.
4. To assemble the salad, place the kale in a large bowl.
5. Top it with the quinoa, grapes, and feta cheese.
6. Pour the dressing on top of the salad and gently toss to combine.
7. Serve immediately.

Per serving: Calories: 225 Protein: 4g Carbs: 16g Fiber: 2g Sugar: 2g Fat: 16g

Gluten Free Chicken Vermicelli & Tomato Salad

SERVES 4 / PREP TIME: 10 MINUTES / COOK TIME: NA

Simply throw together a few raw and prepared ingredients for this tasty dish.

½ red bell pepper, diced
4 large tomatoes, sliced
1 cup romaine lettuce, chopped
2 (5 oz) cooked chicken breasts, sliced
2 tbsp low FODMAP pesto
2 tbsp lactose free sour cream
(optional)
2 cups rice vermicelli, cooked
according to package

1 tbsp fresh basil, torn
1 tbsp olive oil
salt to taste

1. For the salad, mix the red pepper with the tomatoes, lettuce, and chicken in a medium bowl.
2. In a separate bowl, mix the pesto and the lactose free sour cream.
3. Stir the cooked vermicelli into the pesto mix.
4. Lay the pasta on plates.
5. Serve a portion of the salad on the side next to the pasta.
6. Drizzle the salad with the olive oil and sprinkle on the basil, salt, and pepper.

Hint: Use the pesto recipe that appears earlier in this book.

Per serving: Calories: 298 Protein: 25g Carbs: 26g Sugar: 4g Fat: 10g

Tropical Rice

SERVES 5 / PREP TIME: 15 MINUTES / COOK TIME: 2 HOURS SLOW COOKER

This tastes amazing with curries, grilled meats and fish.

2 cups of jasmine rice
2 cups of water
1 cup of canned pineapple, diced
juice of 1 lime
1 crushed lemongrass stem

1. Add the rice, water, pineapple bits, lime juice, and lemongrass into the slow cooker.
2. Set the slow cooker to HIGH.
3. Remove the lemongrass before serving.

Per serving: Calories: 247 Protein: 3g Carbs: 22g Sugar: 4g Fat: 17g

DRINKS AND DESSERTS

Strawberry & Carob Shake

SERVES 1 / PREP TIME: 5 MINUTES / COOK TIME: NA

Think chocolate covered strawberries in a glass!

1/2 cup strawberries, washed and
sliced
1 pasteurised egg white
1/4 cup vanilla soy milk
1 tbsp carob powder

---

1. Combine ingredients in a blender or smoothie maker until smooth.
2. Pour over ice if desired.

Per serving: Calories: 163 Protein: 7g Carbs: 36g Sugar: 20g Fat: 1g

Moroccan Mint Tea

SERVES 6 / PREP TIME: 5 MINUTES / COOK TIME: NA

Mint tea is enjoyed as a refreshing drink in Morocco and is packed with goodness.

2 cups packed fresh mint leaves
6 cups boiling water
4 slices lemon

1. Place all ingredients in a teapot, and stir.
2. Let steep 4 minutes.
3. Stir well and add maple syrup if desired. Serve hot or chilled.

Per serving (without maple syrup): Calories: 0 Protein: 0g Carbs: 0 Sugar: 0g Fat: 0g

Chocolate Banana Smoothie

SERVES 1 / PREP TIME: 5 MINUTES / COOK TIME: NA

A family fave!

1/2 banana, peeled and sliced
1/2 cup rice milk
1 tbsp baking cocoa powder,
unsweetened
1 tsp vanilla extract
handful ice cubes or crushed ice
1 tbsp pure maple syrup (optional)

---

1. Place all of the ingredients into a blender.
2. Blend until smooth, making sure no ice chunks remain.
3. Transfer it to a serving glass and drink at once.

Per serving: Calories: 175 Protein: 2g Carbs: 39g Fiber: 4g Sugar: 29g Fat: 2g

Fruity Mint Virgin Cocktail

SERVES 1 / PREP TIME: 5 MINUTES / COOK TIME: NA

This sweet drink makes a nice addition to a hot summer afternoon.

1 cup cranberry juice, no sugar added
½ cup frozen raspberries
2 fresh mint sprigs, to serve

1. Place all the ingredients into a blender.
2. Pulse until the consistency is smooth.
3. Pour the cocktail into glasses.
4. Serve it topped with fresh mint.

Per serving: Calories: 149 Protein: 2g Carbs: 38g Fiber: 4g Sugar: 29g Fat: 1g

Blueberry Vanilla Milkshake

SERVES 1 / PREP TIME: 10 MINUTES / COOK TIME: NA

This scrumptious milkshake is both healthy and satisfying.

½ cup organic blueberries
1 tsp vanilla extract
1 cup almond milk
1 handful crushed ice

1. In a blender, pulse together the blueberries, maple syrup, vanilla extract, cashew milk, and ice.
2. Pour the shake into two milkshake glasses.
3. Enjoy with a straw.

Per serving: Calories: 147 Protein: 2g Carbs: 27g Fiber: 3g Sugar: 23g Fat: 3g

Tropical Fruit Shake

SERVES 4 / PREP TIME: 10 MINUTES / COOK TIME: NA

Satisfy your sweet tooth with this tasty shake!

---

1 cup crushed ice
½ cup almond/cashew milk
1/2 ripe banana, cut into chunks
3 whole strawberries, stems removed
and halved
¼ cup organic raspberries, plus extra
to garnish

---

1. Add the ice to the blender and crush it until it is in fine pieces.
2. When the ice is ready, add all the ingredients to the blender.
3. Blend the mixture on the "smoothie" setting for approximately 1 minute.
4. Pour into a glass to serve and add one or two raspberries as garnish.

Per serving: Calories: 127 Protein: 2g Carbs: 28g Fiber: 5g Sugar: 18g Fat: 2g

Raspberry & Almond Cake

SERVES 8 / PREP TIME: 20 MINUTES/ COOK TIME: 30 MINUTES

Raspberries and almonds blend into this divine cake.

---

2 cups fresh raspberries
1/2 cup almonds, finely ground
1/4 cup packed brown sugar
8 plus 1 tbsp rice flour
3 large egg whites
1/8 teaspoon salt

8 tbsp canola oil
1 tsp vanilla extract
1/2 tsp almond extract
1 tsp granulated sugar

---

1. Preheat oven to 375F.
2. Cook fresh raspberries in a small saucepan with 1 tbsp. water.
3. Bring to a boil and reduce the heat, simmering until just soft (5 minutes).
4. Spray a 5 inch non-stick springform pan with cooking oil and set aside.
5. In a medium bowl whisk together almonds, brown sugar, and flour until well combined.
6. In a separate large bowl beat the egg whites with salt to form stiff peaks and fold in the nut mixture from earlier.
7. Now fold in the oil, vanilla extract, and almond extract, and spread the batter in the pan.
8. Spread the raspberries evenly over the batter and sprinkle with granulated sugar.
9. Bake for 20-30 minutes or until a knife comes out clean from the centre.
10. Remove and cool on a wired rack.
11. Portion up and serve.

Per serving: Calories: 281 Protein: 5g Carbs: 23g Fiber: 4g Sugar: 9 g Fat: 20g

Chocolate Pudding

SERVES 3 / PREP TIME: 30 MINUTES/ COOK TIME: 10 MINUTES

Satisfy your chocolate cravings with this dessert.

---

3 tbsp granulated sugar
1/4 cup unsweetened cocoa powder
3 tbsp cornstarch
A pinch of salt
3 large pasteurised egg whites
3 cups vanilla soy/rice milk

3 tbsp maple syrup
1/2 tbsp vanilla extract

---

1. Whisk together the sugar, cocoa powder, and cornstarch in a large heatproof glass bowl.
2. In a separate small bowl beat the egg whites until lightly frothy and set aside.
3. Gradually whisk the milk and maple syrup into the cocoa powder mix until well blended.
4. Bring a pan of water to the boil over a high heat and place the glass bowl over the top, whilst whisking constantly until the mixture reaches a boil.
5. Continue whisking for one more minute then remove from heat.
6. Carefully whisk several large spoonfuls of hot pudding into the egg whites to temper.
7. Add the egg mixture back to the glass bowl and whisk well to thoroughly blend.
8. Return the pan to the heat and whisk constantly for one minute until mixture thickens.
9. Remove from heat and whisk in vanilla extract.
10. Pour into three serving glasses and chill until cold.

Per serving: Calories: 243 Protein: 11g Carbs: 43g Fiber: 3g Sugar: 36 g Fat: 5g

Fat-Free Ginger Maple Cookies

SERVES 12 COOKIES / PREP TIME: 10 MINUTES/ COOK TIME: 10 MINUTES

These easy gluten free cookies might just become your new favorite snack!

---

1 cup rice flour
½ tsp baking soda
¼ tsp salt
1/4 tsp ground ginger
½ cup pure maple syrup
2 egg whites

---

1. Preheat the oven to 350 degrees.
2. Sift the dry ingredients together and set aside.
3. In a large bowl, combine the maple syrup and egg whites.
4. Add the dry ingredients to this bowl.
5. Mix the batter together.
6. Now place tablespoons of dough on a cookie sheet lined with parchment paper.
7. Use a fork to press each cookie ball down, forming a cross pattern.
8. Place the sheet in the oven for 5-10 minutes.

Per serving: Calories: 86 Protein: 1g Carbs: 19g Fiber: 0g Sugar: 9 gFat: 0g

Cranberry Orange Oatmeal Cookies

SERVES 12 COOKIES / PREP TIME: 10 MINUTES/ COOK TIME: 10 MINUTES

These scrumptious cookies may take a little longer to bake, but they are well worth it!

1 cup oat flour
1/2 cup cornmeal
1/2 tsp baking powder
1 overripe banana, mashed
1/4 cup coconut sugar
1 large egg white
1 tsp vanilla extract

1/2 tsp ground cloves
1 tsp orange zest
1/4 cup organic cranberries, finely chopped

1. In a medium bowl, mix together the oat flour, cornmeal, and baking powder.
2. In another bowl, beat the banana and sugar until creamy.
3. Add in the egg white, vanilla, cinnamon, and cloves until blended.
4. Add in the flour and cornmeal mixture gradually, until it is creamy.
5. Fold in the zest and cranberries.
6. Roll the dough out onto parchment paper and form it into a 2-inch diameter roll.
7. Place the roll of dough in the refrigerator until it is firm, or about 2 hours.
8. When ready to bake, preheat the oven to 350 degrees.
9. Slice the dough into 1/4inch slices.
10. Place the cookies on a baking sheet lined with parchment paper.
11. Bake for about 10 minutes.
12. Let the cookies cool before serving.

Hint: The 2-inch dough roll will be about 14 inches long with flat edges, so it will have more of a square shape.

Per serving: Calories: 118 Protein: 3g Carbs: 24g Sugar: 6g Fat: 1g

Classic Blueberry Muffins

SERVES 4 / PREP TIME: 5 MINUTES / COOK TIME: 20 MINUTES

These yummy muffins make the perfect breakfast addition!

---

1 ripe mashed banana
1/2 cup coconut sugar
3 egg whites
2 cups gluten-free all purpose baking flour
¼ cup blueberries

¼ cup unsweetened coconut flakes
1/2 cup cashew milk
1 tsp vanilla extract

---

1. Preheat the oven to 350 degrees.
2. Mix the banana and the sugar together until it becomes a creamy paste.
3. Now add in the egg whites and whisk until it is light and fluffy.
4. Fold in the flour using a wooden spoon or spatula.
5. Once the flour is completely mixed in, add the blueberries and most of the coconut flakes.
6. If the mixture is dry, add the milk slowly to ensure the mixture stays moist.
7. Spoon the mixture into a muffin pan lined with muffin papers.
8. Sprinkle the remaining coconut on top of the muffins.
9. Place it in the oven for around 20 minutes.
10. Once baked, the muffins should be springy to the touch.
11. When they are done, leave them to cool and enjoy!

Per serving: Calories: 116 Protein: 2g Carbs: 25g Sugar: 10g Fat: 1g

Chocolatey Coconut Meringues

SERVES 16 MERINGUES / PREP TIME: 15 MINUTES / COOK TIME:8 MINUTES

These little bite-size chocolate cookies will melt in your mouth!

---

3 egg whites
3/4 cup coconut sugar, finely ground in
spice or coffee grinder
3/4 cup unsweetened cocoa powder
¼ cup unsweetened coconut flakes
1/2 tsp vanilla extract
1 pinch sea salt

---

1. Preheat the oven to 350 degrees.
2. Line a cookie sheet with parchment paper.
3. In a medium bowl, whisk the egg whites until they form fluffy soft peaks.
4. Gradually whisk in the sugar, cocoa powder, coconut, vanilla, and sea salt.
5. Drop the meringues by the teaspoonful onto the baking sheets.
6. Try to form approx. 15 small cookies.
7. Bake for about 8 minutes. They should be a little puffed up with a slight crust on top of each cookie.

Per serving: Calories: 53 Protein: 2g Carbs: 12g Sugar: 9g Fat: 1g

Old Fashioned Raspberry Pancakes

SERVES 4 / PREP TIME: 5 MINUTES / COOK TIME: 15 MINUTES

These out flour pancakes might shock you with how delicious they are!

1/2 cup pure maple syrup
1 cup fresh or frozen raspberries
1 cup old fashioned rolled oats (gluten-free)
¼ tsp sea salt

1 tsp baking powder
1/2 cup cashew milk
1 egg white
1 tsp vanilla extract
1 tsp coconut oil

---

1. Warm the maple syrup and raspberries in a small saucepan over medium heat, stirring frequently, until the raspberries have thawed (if using frozen), about 3 minutes.
2. Take the pan off the heat and set aside.
3. Now place the oats and salt in a blender or a food processor and pulse until the consistency is that of coarse flour.
4. Pour the oat flour into a bowl and stir in the salt, and baking powder.
5. In a measuring cup, whisk together the cashew milk, egg white, and vanilla.
6. Then stir this wet mixture into the oats until thoroughly combined. (If the batter thickens too much, add more milk. Do not let this batter rest, as it will thicken quickly.)
7. Pour half the oil onto a smooth, non-stick griddle.
8. Put the griddle on medium heat and, when hot, add the batter.
9. Use a 1/4 cup measure to do this, but only fill it two-thirds full.
10. Cook about 4 pancakes at a time.
11. Cook for 2 minutes on both sides.
12. When you've cooked the first batch, pile them on a plate and cover with a clean tea towel.
13. Oil the pan again and continue cooking.
14. Serve immediately with the warm raspberry maple syrup poured on top.

Per serving: Calories: 218 Protein: 4g Carbs: 46g Sugar: 29g Fat: 3g

Gluten Free Chocolate Cake

SERVES 8 / PREP TIME: 10 MINUTES / COOK TIME: 45 MINUTES

You can still indulge once in a while!

1/2 cup unsweetened cocoa powder, sifted
1/2 cup boiling water
2 tsp vanilla extract
Gluten-free all purpose baking flour (double the volume of egg whites once measured)
½ tsp baking soda
1/4 tsp ground cinnamon

1 pinch salt
3/4 cup coconut sugar
1/2 cup coconut oil, plus extra for greasing
4 egg whites

---

1. Preheat the oven to 325 degrees.
2. Grease a 9-inch spring form cake pan with a little oil or line it with parchment paper.
3. Sift the cocoa powder into a bowl and whisk in the boiling water until you have a smooth but still runny paste.
4. Whisk in the vanilla extract, then set aside to cool.
5. In another small bowl, combine the flour with the baking soda, cinnamon, cayenne, and the pinch of salt.
6. Beat the sugar, coconut oil, and egg whites together in an electric mixer vigorously for about 3 minutes, or until it becomes a thickened cream.
7. Turn the speed down a little and pour in the cocoa mixture, beating as you go.
8. When it is all mixed, you can slowly pour in the flour mixture.
9. Pour this dark, liquid batter into the prepared pan.
10. Bake for 40-45 minutes, or until the sides are set and the centre looks slightly damp. A toothpick should come out clean but with a few crumbs clinging to it.
11. Let it cool for 10 minutes on a wire rack.
12. Then scrape the sides of the cake with a butter knife and spring it out of the pan.
13. Serve either warm or cool.

Per serving: Calories: 258 Protein: 4g Carbs: 33g Sugar: 18g Fat: 15g

Minty Lime Sorbet

SERVES 4 / PREP TIME: 20 MINUTES / CHILLING TIME: 4 HOURS

This strong mint and lime sorbet will delight the tongue after any meal!

¼ cup coconut sugar
2 cups boiling water
8 limes, juice only
4 limes, zest only
20 fresh mint leaves, minced

1 dash sea salt
1 cup water

1. Make the sugar syrup by heating the sugar in 2 cups of boiling water until the sugar dissolves, about 5 minutes.
2. Set it aside to cool down.
3. Once it is cool, combine the syrup with the lime juice, zest, mint leaves, sea salt, and water.
4. Pour this mixture into a container and place it in the fridge for about 30 minutes.
5. After it is thoroughly chilled, put the sorbet base in a flat freezer-safe container, cover it with a lid, and place it in the freezer.
6. After about 45 minutes, take out and churn the sorbet with a fork, evening out what has started to freeze.
7. Return the sorbet to the freezer.
8. Repeat the churning every 45 minutes for at least 3-4 hours.

Per serving: Calories: 66 Protein: 0g Carbs: 19g Sugar: 14g Fat: 0g

Simple Orange-Pineapple Sorbet

SERVES 8 / PREP TIME: 5 MINUTES / CHILLING TIME: 4 HOURS

This 3-ingredient sorbet is so easy, you'll wonder why you haven't been making your own sorbet all along!

1 small pineapple, peeled, cored, and cubed
2 tbsp fresh orange juice
1 cup plus 2 tbsp coconut sugar
1 sprig fresh mint to serve

1. Place the pineapple and orange juice in a food processor.
2. Process this mixture until it is smooth.
3. Add the sugar and process for 1 minute, or until the sugar dissolves.
4. Refrigerate this sorbet base until it is thoroughly chilled.
5. After it has become cold, put it in a flat freezer-safe container, cover it, and put in the freezer.
6. After about 45 minutes, take it out and churn the sorbet with a fork, evening out what has started to freeze.
7. Return the sorbet to the freezer.
8. Repeat the churning every 45 minutes or so for at least 3-4 hours.
9. To serve, garnish each dish with a mint leaf.

Per serving: Calories: 118 Protein: 0g Carbs: 27g Sugar: 27g Fat: 0g

Raspberry and Passion Fruit Sorbet

SERVES 8 / PREP TIME: 20 MINUTES / CHILLING TIME: 3 HOURS

This brightly flavored sorbet can easily be churned in an ice cream maker.

---

4 cups raspberries, fresh or frozen
1 cup passion-fruit, juiced
3/4 to 1 cup coconut sugar
1 dash sea salt
3 tbsp lemon juice

---

1. Place the raspberries, passionfruit juice, 3/4 cup of the sugar, salt, and lemon juice into a blender.
2. Purée everything until it is very well blended.
3. Taste the mixture for tartness, and add more sugar if necessary, blending well.
4. Strain the mixture through a fine mesh sieve to remove the raspberry seeds.
5. Chill the mixture if it's not already cold.
6. Pour the mixture into an ice cream maker and freeze according to the directions.
7. After churning, place the sorbet in the freezer for 2-3 hours to finish freezing completely.
8. If not using an ice cream maker, pour the ingredients into a container and place it in the freezer for 30 minutes. Remove and stir it well with a fork.
9. Continue to freeze the mixture, stirring well every half hour until the sorbet is frozen to the desired texture.

Per serving: Calories: 141 Protein: 1g Carbs: 36g Sugar: 31g Fat: 1g

Simple Lemon Crepes

SERVES 4 / PREP TIME: 20 MINUTES / COOK TIME: 5 MINUTES

All you need is a little lemon juice to make these crepes fabulous!

---

1 cup rice flour, sifted
1 pinch of salt
2 egg whites
1 dash vanilla extract
1 cup unsweetened light coconut milk
1 tbsp coconut oil

---

1. Sift the rice flour, and salt into a large mixing bowl.
2. Make a well in the centre of the flour and add the egg whites.
3. Begin whisking the egg whites.
4. Next gradually add the vanilla and the coconut milk, still whisking.
5. When all the liquid has been added, whisk until the batter is smooth and has the consistency of thin cream.
6. Meanwhile, heat the coconut oil in a non-stick skillet or crepe maker until it is hot.
7. Get the pan really hot, then turn the heat down to medium.
8. Spoon out two tablespoons of batter onto the skillet.
9. As soon as the batter hits the hot pan, tip it around from side to side to get the bottom evenly coated with batter.
10. Cook on each side for about 30 second. Lift the edge with a butter knife to see if the bottom is golden brown before turning.
11. Flip the crepe over with a spatula, cook for 30 seconds, and slide it out onto a plate.
12. Stack the crepes as you make them between sheets of parchment paper.
13. Keep them warm by placing the pancake platter on top of a bowl filled with boiling water.
14. To serve, sprinkle each crepe with freshly squeezed lemon juice and coconut sugar.
15. Fold them in half, then in half again to form triangles. You may also simply roll them up.
16. Serve them sprinkled with a little more sugar and lemon juice with a wedge of lemon on the side.

Per serving: Calories: 183 Protein: 4g Carbs: 25g Sugar: 1g Fat: 8g

Gluten Free Glazed Lemon Donuts

SERVES 4 / PREP TIME: 30 MINUTES / COOK TIME: 20 MINUTES

These baked gluten free donuts can compete with store-bought ones any day!

---

cup coconut sugar
2 tbsp coconut oil
3 egg whites
1/2 cup plain coconut milk yogurt
1 tsp lemon zest
1 tsp vanilla extract
½ cup rice flour
cup tapioca starch
1/4 cup golden flax meal

1 tsp baking powder
½ tsp salt
1 cup coconut sugar, finely ground in a spice or coffee grinder
2 tbsp lemon juice
1 tbsp plain coconut milk yogurt
1 tbsp lemon zest

---

1. Preheat the oven to 325 degrees.
2. In a large bowl, whisk the sugar with the oil for 2 minutes.
3. Add in the egg whites and beat the mixture until the batter starts to bubble.
4. Add in the yogurt, lemon zest, and vanilla extract and combine.
5. In another bowl, combine the flour, tapioca starch, flax meal, baking powder, and salt.
6. Slowly add this to the batter, beating until completely blended.
7. Spoon the batter into a donut pan or donut molds and bake for 15-20 minutes, or until golden.
8. Remove from the oven and leave it to cool for 10 minutes before popping the donuts out of their molds.
9. For the lemon glaze, whisk together the ground sugar and lemon juice until they are smooth.
10. Add in the yogurt and whisk well.
11. Dip each donut into the glaze and sprinkle them with lemon zest to serve.

Per serving: Calories: 479 Protein: 5g Carbs: 93g Sugar: 67g Fat: 10g

Pina Colada Sorbet

SERVES 2 / PREP TIME: 5 MINUTES / COOK TIME: 10 MINUTES

Tropical dessert.

---

1 cup canned pineapple, diced
1 cup almond milk
1/4 cup desiccated coconut,
unsweetened
2 sprigs fresh mint

---

1. Blend pineapple with almond milk and coconut until smooth.
2. Pour into a plastic container cover.
3. Place in the freezer for 2 hours.
4. Stir and replace for another 2 hours.
5. If set, serve immediately in a tall glass with a sprig of fresh mint.
6. If still a little sludgy, stir again and leave for a further hour.

Per serving: Calories: 88 Protein: 1g Carbs: 16g Sugar: 13g Fat: 3g

Orange Cranberry Cookies

SERVES 6 / PREP TIME: 20 MINUTES / COOK TIME: 10 MINUTES

Treat yourself!

½ tsp baking powder
1 cup rice flour
¼ cup caster sugar
1 tsp vanilla extract
2 egg whites
¼ cup organic cranberries, chopped
1 small mashed banana (very ripe)
1 orange, juice and zest

---

1.   Mix together the baking powder, flour and sugar in a medium bowl.
2.   Use another bowl to beat together the sugar and banana until the consistency is creamy.
3.   Then, add the vanilla and egg into the bowl and mix well.
4.   Now fold the wet ingredients into the dry ingredients.
5.   Fold in the orange zest and the cranberries.
6.   Use your hands to form a dough ball.
7.   Let the dough chill in the refrigerator for about 2 hours until firm.
8.   Then, roll out the dough onto parchment paper and use cookie cutters to cut out your cookies, collecting the leftover dough and rolling out once more to cut as many cookies as you can.
9.   Preheat your oven to 350f/150c/gas mark 2.
10. Bake the cookies for 10 minutes and then allow to cool before serving.

Per serving: Calories: 159 Protein: 3g Carbs: 36g Sugar: 12g Fat: 0g

No Bake Lemon Raspberry Cheesecake with Gingersnap Crusts

SERVES 6 / PREP TIME: 20 MINUTES / CHILL TIME: 3 HOURS

Talk about the perfect balance of easy and delicious!

15 gluten free ginger snap cookies
coconut oil for greasing
1/3 cup coconut oil
5 oz lactose free cream cheese
2 tbsp pure maple syrup
1 tsp vanilla extract
1/2 lemon, juiced
3/4 cup organic raspberries

1. To make the crust, gently pulse the ginger snaps and coconut oil in a food processor until the mixture has the consistency of sand.
2. Spread this mixture into a spring form pan, pie pan, or 8x8 baking dish greased generously with coconut oil.
3. Press the mixture down, smoothing with the back of a spoon until the crust is flat and even.
4. Put the pan in the fridge to firm up while you make the cheesecake layer.
5. Add the rest of the ingredients except the raspberries to the food processor and pulse until the mixture is smooth and creamy.
6. Mix in the raspberries by hand and set the processor bowl to the side.
7. Next, remove the crust from the fridge.
8. Spread the cheesecake filling evenly on top of the crust.
9. Cover the cheesecake with plastic wrap.
10. Return the pan to the fridge to get cold and firm, about 3 hours.
11. Remove the cheesecake from the fridge 10 minutes before serving.
12. Slice it into 12 bars and enjoy.

Per serving: Calories: 286 Protein: 3g Carbs: 23g Sugar: 15g Fat: 23g

Blueberry Rice Pudding

SERVES 6 / PREP TIME: 10 MINUTES / COOK TIME: 1.5 HOURS SLOW COOKER

Tastes great with blueberries or any low fodmap fruit of your choice.

---

2 cups of cooked white rice
1 tsp vanilla extract
4 cups of almond milk
maple syrup, to taste
1 cup of blueberries

---

1. Stir the rice milk, vanilla extract, and rice in the slow cooker pot.
2. Set the slow cooker on HIGH.
3. To serve, stir in a little maple syrup with the blueberries.

Per serving (without maple syrup): Calories: 249 Protein: 3g Carbs: 44g Fiber: 2g
Sugar: 19g Fat: 3g

Slow-Cooked Fruit Crumble

SERVES 6 / PREP TIME: 10 MINUTES / COOK TIME: 2-3 HOURS SLOW COOKER

A perfect summer dessert.

---

3 cups of sliced strawberries
2 cups of sliced banana
1 tbsp of grated lemon zest
1 cup of gluten-free oats
¼ tsp of ground cinnamon

---

1. Mix the strawberries, banana, and lemon zest, and place them in the slow cooker.
2. Mix the oats with the ground cinnamon, and top over the fruits.
3. Set the slow cooker to HIGH for 2-3 hours or until crumble is golden brown.

Per serving: Calories: 96 Protein: 3g Carbs: 20g Sugar: 7g Fat: 1g

Old-Fashioned Blueberry Crumble

SERVES 4 / PREP TIME: 10 MINUTES / COOK TIME: 40 MINUTES

Delicious blueberries simmer under a layer of sweet oats in this gluten free dessert.

2 1/4 cups organic blueberries
2 tbsp water
1 tbsp cornstarch
3 tbsp coconut oil, melted
2/3 cup old fashioned rolled oats (gluten-free)
3 tbsp fresh ground oat flour
1 pinch of salt
1 dash vanilla extract

2 tbsp pure maple syrup

1. Heat the oven to 350 degrees.
2. Heat the blueberries in a small pan over low heat on the stovetop until they have softened.
3. Add the water and cornstarch to the blueberries.
4. Stir well and leave the berries to simmer for 2 minutes on low heat.
5. Meanwhile, melt the coconut oil.
6. Put the oats, oat flour, melted coconut oil, salt, vanilla extract, and maple syrup together in a bowl and stir.
7. Pour the blueberries into a 9x13 baking dish and spread the crumble on top.
8. Bake the crumble for 30-35 minutes in the oven, or until the top has become crunchy and brown.

Per serving: Calories: 249 Protein: 3g Carbs: 35g Fiber: 4g Sugar: 15g Fat: 12g

Chocolate Quinoa Pudding Bars

SERVES 8 / PREP TIME: 10 MINUTES / COOK TIME: 25 MINUTES

Yum!

---

2 egg whites
¾ cup brown sugar
½ cup quinoa
1/4 cup cocoa powder, unsweetened
1 small very ripe mashed banana
¼ cup rice flour
1 tsp baking powder
1 tsp vanilla extract

---

1. Preheat your oven to 350f/150c/gas mark 2.
2. Line an 8-inch pan with parchment paper.
3. Mix the banana, egg whites, brown sugar and vanilla.
4. Now mix in the quinoa, brown rice flour and baking powder.
5. Fold in the cocoa powder and then spread the batter out across the prepared pan.
6. Flatten the top with a cooking spatula or knife.
7. Bake for 25 minutes.
8. Allow the batter to cool before slicing into bars.

Per serving: Calories: 169 Protein: 3g Carbs: 39g Sugar: 24g Fat: 1g

CONVERSION TABLES

Volume

Imperial	Metric
1 tbsp	15ml
2 fl oz	55 ml
3 fl oz	75 ml
5 fl oz (¼ pint)	150 ml
10 fl oz (½ pint)	275 ml
1 pint	570 ml
1 ¼ pints	725 ml
1 ¾ pints	1 litre
2 pints	1.2 litres
2½ pints	1.5 litres
4 pints	2.25 litres

Oven temperatures

Gas Mark	Fahrenheit	Celsius
1/4	225	110
1/2	250	130
1	275	140
2	300	150
3	325	170
4	350	180
5	375	190
6	400	200
7	425	220
8	450	230
9	475	240

Weight

Imperial	Metric
½ oz	10 g
¾ oz	20 g
1 oz	25 g
1½ oz	40 g
2 oz	50 g
2½ oz	60 g
3 oz	75 g
4 oz	110 g
4½ oz	125 g
5 oz	150 g
6 oz	175 g
7 oz	200 g
8 oz	225 g
9 oz	250 g
10 oz	275 g
12 oz	350 g

BIBLIOGRAPHY

FODMAP food list (2017) Available at: http://www.ibsdiets.org/fodmap-diet/fodmap-food-list/ (Accessed: 22 February 2017).

Micawber (no date) Dangers of avoidance. Available at: http://www.ibs-health.com/page284.html (Accessed: 22 February 2017).

Ross, E. and Lam, M. (2016) 'The low FODMAPS diet and IBS: A winning strategy', Journal of Clinical Nutrition & Dietetics, 02(01). doi: 10.4172/2472-1921.100013.

Camilleri, M. and Acosta, A. (2014) 'Re: Halmos et al, A diet low in FODMAPs reduces symptoms of irritable bowel syndrome', Gastroenterology, 146(7), pp. 1829–1830. doi: 10.1053/j.gastro.2014.01.071.

Gibson, P.R., Varney, J.E. and Muir, J.G. (2016) 'Diet therapy for irritable bowel syndrome: Is a diet low in FODMAPS really similar in efficacy to traditional dietary advice?', Gastroenterology, 150(4), pp. 1046–1047. doi: 10.1053/j.gastro.2015.10.053.

Piacentino, D., Rossi, S., Piretta, L., Badiali, D., Pallotta, N. and Corazziari, E. (2016) 'Tu1425 role of FODMAPs, and benefit of Low-FODMAP diet, in irritable bowel syndrome severity', Gastroenterology, 150(4), p. S901. doi: 10.1016/s0016-5085(16)33048-7.

Chung, C.-Y. and Joo, Y.-E. (2014) 'Can a diet low in Fermentable Oligosaccharides, Disaccharides, Monosaccharides and polyols (FODMAPs) reduce the symptoms of irritable bowel syndrome?', The Korean Journal of Gastroenterology, 64(2), p. 123. doi: 10.4166/kjg.2014.64.2.123.

BS: Risk of IBS increases after bacterial infection (2015) Nature Reviews Gastroenterology & Hepatology, 12(6), pp. 313–313. doi: 10.1038/nrgastro.2015.86.

Sidebar (1998) Available at: http://www.aboutibs.org (Accessed: 23 February 2017).

Index

Made in the USA
San Bernardino, CA
17 October 2018